WHAT'S ECOLOGY?

Lawrence W. McCombs
Nicholas Rosa

▲ ADDISON-WESLEY PUBLISHING COMPANY

Menlo Park, California ● Reading, Massachusetts ● London ● Don Mills, Ontario

Table of Contents

1

Living Things and Their Surroundings

Man's Place in Nature

Modern western man has generally regarded himself as the master of the earth. He has seen himself as distinct from nature, which included all other living things. With his great inventiveness, he has achieved great power over nature. Men of Biblical times dreamed of moving mountains; modern man can move them. Over thousands of years of civilization, man has used plants, animals, soils, water, and minerals in any way he saw fit. Even if his activities caused total destruction, he paid little heed.

Today, as man's numbers are rapidly multiplying, he is beginning to see that there are limits to what he can safely do. Thus, as power has grown so has understanding. But understanding is sadly lagging behind man's ability to destroy. Beginning with scientists, philosophers, and a mystic here and there, people are coming to realize that man is a part of nature. Thus, it has begun to dawn on man that he can be his own worst enemy. As the cartoon character Pogo said, "We have met the enemy and he is us."

In recent years, many people have begun to question what our place in nature really is. How are we related to other living organisms and to the planet we live on? What effects do our actions have on the environment? In the opinion of many scientists, our very survival may soon depend on finding the proper answers to these questions.

Over the past century, scientists have become more and more aware of the close ties between living organisms and their environment. Each plant and animal lives in a delicate balance with other living things. Climate, soil, water supplies, and available chemicals all affect the organisms as well. A single event may seem at first to affect only one kind of creature. Yet it may set off a chain of changes that greatly alter the entire picture.

A hundred years ago, the Kaibab forest on the north rim of the Grand Canyon in Arizona was one of the most beautiful forests in the country. About 4000 mule deer lived among the pine, fir, and spruce trees. Indians hunted the deer each fall. They used the deer for both food and clothing. Mountain lions, wolves, and coyotes also lived by hunting the deer.

In 1906 the forest was made a National Game Preserve. To protect the deer, hunting was forbidden. Government bounty hunters killed most of the animals that preyed upon the deer. At first the program seemed very successful. By 1925, more than 6000 of the predator animals had been killed. The deer population had grown amazingly. Some 100,000 deer were living in the forest.

But by that time a new danger to the deer had become clear. There were so many deer in the forest that the forest itself was being literally eaten away. All of the shrubs and the lower branches of the trees, as high as a deer could reach, were stripped bare of leaves and twigs. This meant much less food for many more deer. Two harsh winters proved disastrous for the starving herd. Thousands died. By 1930 only about 25,000 deer were left. The population of deer continued to drop. By 1942 only about 8000 deer survived. These were mostly smaller, weaker deer than their ancestors in the 1906 herd.

The forest itself was no longer the same. Most of the young trees had been destroyed during the years of high deer population. Some plants, such as willow trees and

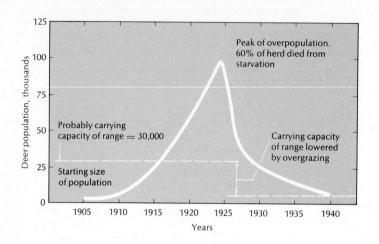

Figure 1–1

The graph shows what happened to the deer population in the Kaibab forest after their natural enemies started to be killed off in 1905. Notice that the carrying capacity—the number of deer the forest can support—was ultimately reduced from 30,000 to about 5000.

Figure 1–2

The photo at the left, taken in the Kaibab forest in 1925, shows the effects of overgrazing. The juniper trees in the foreground have been stripped to a height of over seven feet and the usual sagebrush cover is absent. The photo on the facing page, taken 17 years later, when the deer population had begun to decline, shows considerable recovery of the sagebrush. The junipers have filled in somewhat, but there is still no growth below the seven-foot level.

raspberries, had been destroyed entirely. Certain kinds of grasses and small plants, not favored as food by the deer, had replaced many of the glades of small trees. The remaining deer could not obtain food as easily as did the original herd in the original forest.

It may be many more years before a new balance is achieved. What the new forest and its animal population will be, we do not yet know. The story of the Kaibab forest has been an important object lesson for those who try to improve upon the natural balance of living things. An attempt to help or favor one kind of organism may result in harm.

We are beginning to realize that we need to learn a great deal more about the web of relationships in nature. Today our newspapers, radio, and television carry many stories about man-made changes in the natural system. Insecticides, air and water pollution, widespread farming and lumbering, and the building of highways and cities all are changing the lives of many living things. The survival of many kinds of plants and animals—and perhaps of man himself—may depend upon our achieving a better understanding of what we are doing to our environment.

Ecology: Households, Neighbors, and Neighborhoods

Along with this new awareness of their environment, Americans have gained a "new" word in their everyday language: *ecology*. This is the study of the relationships between living things and their environment. As a science, it is a division of biology. In one way or another, it has always been a part of biology, but has been recognized as a separate field only since about 1900. Its name is derived from an old Greek word, *oikos*, which meant "house" or "home." (The familiar word *economics* has the same root.) An ecologist is concerned with the "households" of living things, with the relationships between "neighbors" and with their interactions with the nonliving surroundings.

The environment of the Kaibab deer included both living and nonliving things. The trees the deer fed upon were an important part of their environment. So were the

wolves, coyotes, mountain lions, and human beings that killed and ate the deer. The light, moisture, temperature, and soils of the forest region were also important in making the life of the deer what it was. Their environment is a "model" of all life-environments: a complex combination of nonliving and living ingredients. And so is man's.

An ecologist would be interested in many things about the Kaibab forest. Which kinds of plants did the deer eat? Did the plants grow rapidly enough to replace the material eaten by the deer? How many deer could live in this forest without serious damage to the plants? That is, what was the true *carrying capacity* of the forest for this animal? It appeared in 1906 that the Kaibab forest could support many more deer, and indeed the deer herd soon multiplied by some 25 times—only to "die back" to a smaller population again.

There is more about this one forest that an ecologist would want to find out. What animals killed and fed upon the deer? How many of these animals could be supported by the 4000 deer originally in the forest? (What, in other words, was the forest's carrying capacity for these predators?) Did the predator animals kill just any deer—or mostly the young, or perhaps the old or the sick deer? Did the deer population remain nearly constant from year to year under the pre-1906 conditions? If not, how and why did it vary?

What limited the population of the animals that fed on deer? Were they in turn eaten by something else, or did they simply die of old age or starvation? After the overpopulation of deer had damaged the forest, how did the new system of plants and animals differ from the old? When the number of deer decreased, did the forest begin to slowly change back to its old form, or has it been permanently altered?

The Kaibab forest is an ecological system, or *ecosystem*. It includes all of the plants and animals of the forest, as well as the soil, air, and water of the area. That is, an ecosystem includes the living organisms, plus their nonliving physical environment. The term *ecosystem* is usually applied only to some part of the earth that is relatively self-sufficient. Of course, almost any ecosystem receives energy directly from the sun. Air and water enter

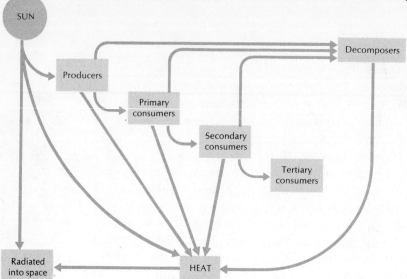

FLOW OF ENERGY

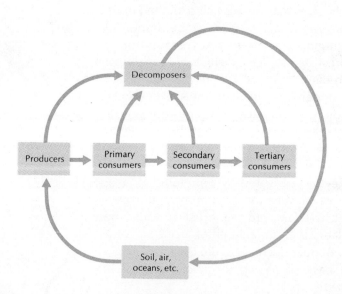

CYCLING OF MATTER

Figure 1–3

Any ecosystem requires a constant input of energy in the form of sunlight. Most sunlight is never used by living things but is simply radiated off into space. And much of the energy taken in by organisms is lost from an ecosystem in the form of heat. Matter, on the other hand, changes and rechanges with essentially no long-term loss.

and leave most ecosystems. Yet a forest is a unit that can be studied quite well by itself. The plants and climate are much the same throughout the forest. The animals in it are those that depend on those particular plants, climate, and other conditions.

A desert area might be studied as another ecosystem. A mountain stream or a lake could be regarded as an ecosystem. A coral atoll, with its regional animals that can live nowhere else, is yet another ecosystem. In the largest example, the entire surface of the earth makes up a huge ecosystem called the *biosphere*. This includes not only the land surface, but the atmosphere and waters, the upper layers of soil, and all the living things of our planet.

Ecosystems can also be quite small. An aquarium may be regarded as a complete ecosystem. A decaying log on the forest floor is an ecosystem, populated chiefly by insects and other tiny organisms.

On the other hand, it is not usually convenient to regard a single tree in the forest as an ecosystem. Most of the animals that live in and on the tree spend major parts of their lives away from the tree. The population of different kinds of animals may vary greatly from day to day, or even from hour to hour. The tree *could* be defined as an ecosystem, but it would be a rather special one, and so not a very useful ecosystem to study.

No ecosystem is really closed or self-sufficient, however. *All ecosystems require an incoming supply of energy*. In any ecosystem, energy enters and energy leaves. Energy takes many forms—light and heat, or the energy of motion in a muscle or an engine, or chemical energy stored in a firecracker or a flashlight cell, and so on. As you know, energy can be transformed from one kind into another.

The original energy from the sun may be stored for a time in living matter as chemical energy, or used as energy of motion, but eventually all energy used becomes heat, which is lost to the system by being radiated away. However, the matter in an ecosystem is usually recycled—used over and over. As many examples in this book will illustrate, _matter cycles, but energy is lost_ in all ecosystems and for the earth as a whole. This is one of the basic principles of biology and ecology.

Food Relationships
in an Ecosystem

Before 1906 the Kaibab forest was apparently a rather stable, well-balanced ecosystem. It included populations of many kinds of plants and animals. The plants used energy from the sun, chemicals from the air and the soil, and water from rainfall and snow to produce their own branches, stems, and leaves.

The green plants are the food makers in the Kaibab or any ecosystem. In the process called *photosynthesis,* plants are able to capture solar energy and use it to produce plant matter from carbon dioxide and water. Thus, they are the *producers* of the ecosystem.

Many animals subsist by eating the plants. The deer browse upon the tender twigs, branches, and buds. Chipmunks and squirrels eat seeds and nuts. Insects of many kinds eat leaves, flowers, wood, and even roots. Some birds feed upon flowers and seeds. Within the soil and overlying leaf litter, various insects, worms, and other small animals eat plant debris. These animals are the *primary consumers* of the ecosystem. They build their own bodies from materials they obtain from the producers. They also get the energy they need for their living activities from the same sources.

Other animals in turn feed upon the primary consumers. In North American forests, wolves, coyotes, mountain lions, and bobcats live by eating deer, squirrels, chipmunks, and perhaps some birds. Snakes and lizards feed upon mice, toads, frogs, birds, and insects. Woodpeckers and other birds feed upon insects. Foxes, weasels, owls, and hawks eat various small animals. These creatures are the *secondary consumers* of the ecosystem.

Some of the hunting animals may even be *tertiary consumers* feeding upon the secondary consumers. Hawks, owls, and foxes may feed upon small meat-eating animals (such as weasels) as well as upon plant-eaters. Among the secondary and tertiary consumers are a number of different scavenger animals—vultures, maggots, some ants, certain beetles, and certain worms, to give a few examples. Unlike predators, scavengers feed mainly on tissue that is already dead. They do not kill for a living.

Eventually we reach the end of such a *food chain*. The hawks, owls, wolves, and mountain lions are not a major source of food for any large animals. Most of these consumers die of old age or by accidents. Yet their flesh is not lost to the system. When they die, their bodies decompose: their tissues are broken down into simpler chemicals. The chemicals are returned to the soil, to be used again by the green plants. Even bone is broken down in this way. This decomposition is carried out by tiny organisms such as bacteria and fungi. These *decomposers* are seldom noticed when we look at the plants and animals of an area. Yet they play a vital role in the functioning of the ecosystem.

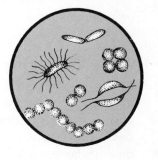

Without the decomposers, all the important chemicals would eventually be tied up in the bodies of living and dead animals. There would be no recycling of materials for use by the producers. The primary consumers would eventually eat up all the plants, and in their turn would all be eaten. The meat-eating animals would eventually run out of food and die. Without the unseen decomposers, the system would not keep operating as it does.

Plants and animals are living elements of an ecosystem. The chemicals, water, and air are the nonliving elements of the ecosystem. Any ecosystem is made up of nonliving elements, plus the producers and consumers as well as decomposers. As you can readily see, the organisms that fill these roles will be quite different in a forest ecosystem, an ocean ecosystem, or a stream ecosystem. Even two different forests may have different kinds of organisms in these roles.

How an Ecologist Does His Work

The importance of ecological studies is being recognized today. The need for more information about ecosystems is clear. What kinds of studies can be made? How does an ecologist gather information? What methods does he use? Like the naturalist, the ecologist must usually begin by observing plants and animals in their natural surroundings. A great deal of careful observation is needed to identify the various organisms and to begin to note the major food chains.

After the food chains have been identified, the ecologist can make more detailed measurements. Populations of various kinds of organisms can be counted. The amounts of various materials and of energy passing through each part of the ecosystem can be calculated. Chemicals such as phosphate and nitrogen can be traced in their movements through the food web. Relationships and dependencies between different kinds of organisms can be worked out. Little by little, understanding of how a particular ecosystem is put together and functions can be developed. This knowledge throws light on how the earth's entire ecosphere functions and what its needs are. But for the moment, suppose we stay with more limited ecosystems, such as forests, to see how an ecologist goes about his work.

Measuring the numbers of each kind of organism in an ecosystem requires more than simple counting, which is not always possible. The ecologist must understand sampling methods and statistical operations. However, with land plants, as in a forest, this kind of measurement, although tedious, is not difficult. Plants do not run away or hide. In a forest, an area of one acre could be measured off. The numbers of each kind of plant in the area could then be counted. These numbers could then be multiplied by the number of acres in the forest to find out the total populations. Of course, even the counting of all of the plants on a single acre would be an almost impossible task. Much smaller areas are usually used, and the forest is sampled in many places. Care must be taken to be sure that the sample areas chosen are typical of the entire forest. Aerial photographs are often used to estimate the total area of a forest.

The counting of animal populations is much more difficult. In the sample area, the presence of human beings is almost certain to cause many animals to hide or to move elsewhere. Some form of trapping or hunting is almost always necessary. Large animals, such as the Kaibab deer, can be counted fairly easily. Surveys from the air, or even on foot, can yield fairly accurate counts. The tiny organisms of the soil, or insects burrowing in plants, can be collected quite easily in representative samples. It is the small- and middle-sized animal populations that pose the difficult problems.

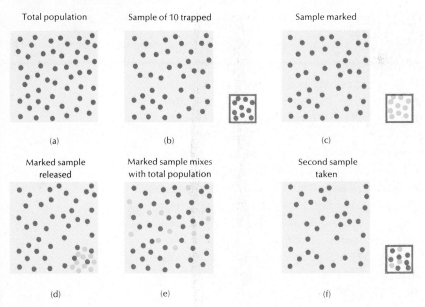

Total population   Sample of 10 trapped   Sample marked

(a)   (b)   (c)

Marked sample released   Marked sample mixes with total population   Second sample taken

(d)   (e)   (f)

Figure 1–4

Trapping and marking a sample is one way of making a count of a population. Based on the second sample of this population taken (*f*), about how many organisms are there in the population?

One common technique involves trapping and marking a sample of the population. For example, a hundred chipmunks might be trapped and marked with metal tags or paint. They are then released. After these chipmunks have had time to spread evenly through the forest, another sample of a hundred chipmunks is trapped. Let us suppose that ten previously-marked chipmunks are found among the second hundred. That is, ten of the new sample had also been trapped in the first sample. If we assume that the released chipmunks spread out randomly through the forest, and that our second sample is also a random sample of the population, it seems clear that our first sample represented about 10 out of each 100 chipmunks in the forest. That is, the total population is about ten times as large as the sample of 100 that we trapped. The total population therefore is about 1000 chipmunks.

Of course, the assumptions are very risky. Chipmunks that have been trapped once may be much more clever at avoiding traps the second time. Also, the chipmunks may not spread out randomly through the forest, but may tend to live in particular trees all their lives. Complicated systems of multiple samplings and mathematical analysis are used to help test the reliability of these methods.

Further information about food chains may come from the study of trapped or killed animals. Stomach contents of dead animals provide information about the kinds of food they ate. Counts may be made of the number of animals that appear to have died from particular diseases.

Still more information can come from the study of captured animals in the laboratory. The amount of food eaten can be measured. The number of young produced each year can easily be counted. Preferences for different kinds of food, different conditions of temperature and moisture, or different sorts of living quarters can be observed. Of course, we must be cautious, for animals do not always behave in captivity in the same way as they do in their natural surroundings.

In later chapters, we shall see many examples of the kinds of information gathered by ecologists and of the methods used to gather that information.

What about man? Is there a study of human ecology? What is our relationship with other organisms and with our physical environment? What can ecological findings tell us about the wisdom of our actions? What is our place in the ecosystem? How can we be sure that we do not accidentally disrupt the ecosystem in many ways that will later prove disastrous to us? We shall look at all this in later chapters.

Ecology is more than another specialized branch of the biological sciences. It is more than a collection of facts and words to be memorized. Ecological studies suggest a new and valuable way of looking at the world. You may find that ecology offers useful insights into many human problems that at first do not appear related to biology.

Also, an ecological point of view makes use of insights from other bodies of knowledge besides biology. Thus, it ties many things together into a meaningful whole. As you read this book, try to think of the world around you in ecological perspectives. The ideas presented here are tools; you may be able to make use of them in creating knowledge and understanding of your environment.

Test Yourself

1. Ecology is a branch of biology, which is the general study of living things. With what aspect of living things is ecology concerned?
2. What two kinds of things make up a living organism's environment?
3. What is an ecosystem?
4. What is photosynthesis? What does this process do?
5. What is a primary consumer?
6. What is meant by "carrying capacity"?
7. What lesson can be learned from the story of the Kaibab deer?
8. What happens to matter and energy in all ecosystems?
9. Are you a part of any food chains? If so, can you name or describe them? At what level of the food chain are you (are you a producer, a consumer, a decomposer)?
10. Would you think of your house as an ecosystem? Your town or city? Is this a useful concept?

Describing an Ecosystem

Major Forest Types

Although forests are not the only kind of ecosystem, suppose we stay with them a while longer. They are still a good starting point for the places we have to go.

At some time you have probably walked in a forest. Try to remember what you saw there. How shall we begin to describe the forest ecosystem in a way that will help us to understand it? Once we can do this, we shall have the tools to help us understand other ecosystems.

The trees are the largest and most obvious living things in the forest. You know, of course, that not all trees are the same. The oak tree is quite different from the pine. We might begin our study of the forest by noting the kinds of trees that grow there.

Refer to the map shown in Figure 2-1, which shows the kinds of vegetation dominant in various parts of North America. As you can see, the *coniferous* (evergreen) forest of Canada stretches all the way across the continent. Spruce and fir trees dominate in the Canadian forest. There is also a coniferous forest belt in the Rocky Mountain region, where ponderosa pine is prevalent. Douglas fir and ponderosa pine characterize the coniferous forest along the Pacific coast. In the area around the Great Lakes and extending along the Appalachians and up into Maine, spruce, fir, and hemlock are common. In this mixed forest area there are also birch, beech, and maple trees, which lose their leaves and are called *hardwood*, or *deciduous*, trees.

Ponderosa

Maple

Farther to the south is the central hardwood forest. On northern slopes and in the valleys, the yellow poplar is dominant. On the drier southern slopes and mountain tops, oak and chestnut make up most of the forest. Along the western edge of the forest oak and hickory dominate.

Along the coastal plains of the Atlantic and Gulf coasts to the south, pine forests are common. However, where these forests are not disturbed by logging or by fires, they may be replaced over a period of years by hardwoods such as hickory, oak, and magnolia.

Hickory

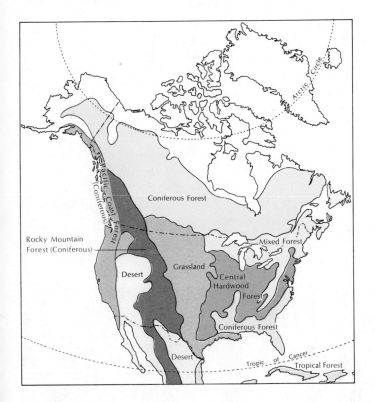

Figure 2–1

The major forest regions of North America.

Of course, each of these kinds of forest could be further subdivided. The divisions between them are not abrupt. There are regions where mixtures of two kinds of forest exist. Yet it is clear that it would be possible to divide the forest into regions based upon the major kinds of trees present.

Would such divisions be useful? Are these different forests different from each other in significant ways?

As you wandered through these forests, you would indeed notice great differences between them. In the coniferous forests of the north, the pines or other evergreen trees form a thick layer overhead throughout the year. Most of the light and rainfall is intercepted by the crowded needles of the trees. Few small trees or shrubs grow in this forest. The ground is covered with a layer of fallen needles and other debris from the trees. Ferns and mosses and a few flowering plants are scattered sparsely over the ground.

The temperature inside the forest is noticeably warmer than that in clearings. Wind is almost entirely blocked by the coniferous forest. You may hear a gale whipping the tops of the trees, but scarcely more than a breeze can be felt on the forest floor.

The hardwood, or deciduous, forests are quite different. Here a much greater amount of light and rainfall

Figure 2–2

Below, a coniferous forest of Engelmann spruce and lodgepole pine in Colorado with a detail of the sparse forest floor. The forest floor shown on the facing page is in a mixed hardwood area in Maryland consisting of oak, poplar, and hickory.

reaches the forest floor, particularly in the winter, when the leaves have fallen from the trees. Although the trees block the wind to a great extent, the wind within a hardwood forest is much stronger than the wind in the coniferous forests of the north.

In a hardwood forest, many kinds of plants grow beneath the tall trees. There are many trees of intermediate height, spreading their leaves below the crowns of the tallest trees. Shrubs about 5 to 15 feet high cover much of the forest floor. Wildflowers and other small plants are common on the ground. In the hardwood forests, the forest floor is usually cooler than the ground temperature in open spaces.

As you might expect, the very different conditions in these two kinds of forest are accompanied by wide differences in animal populations. A great variety of insects and small birds and animals live among the shrubs and small

plants of the southern forest floor. The bare forest floor of the coniferous forest supports a much sparser population of these small creatures. On the other hand, larger animals such as deer, moose, bear, and wolves seem to be more common in the coniferous forests. The particular kinds of birds, insects, and small mammals found in the two forests are for the most part quite different. For example, in a coniferous forest, the typical squirrel is a small seed-eating red squirrel; in a deciduous forest, the typical squirrel is a larger acorn-leaf and nut-eating grey squirrel type.

Layers and Canopies in an Ecosystem

Let's sit in one spot quietly for a while and observe the animals that live in the forest. This could take some time, but if we remain still long enough, the residents of the forest begin to emerge and go about their normal activities. A surprising variety of animal life may appear.

Birds and squirrels flit through the branches and hop about the ground. Turtles, snakes, lizards, mice, chip-

Figure 2–3

A forest can be thought of as being divided into layers, or strata, each of which is frequented by certain kinds of animals. The temperatures on any given day can differ by as much as 28° F from the upper stratum to the soil layer.

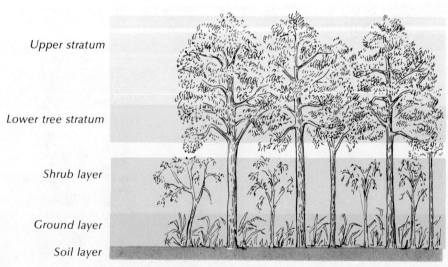

Upper stratum

Lower tree stratum

Shrub layer

Ground layer

Soil layer

Deciduous forest profile

munks, ground squirrels, skunks, rabbits, raccoons, frogs, and rats may be seen moving about the ground. Shrews and moles burrow busily beneath the surface. Weasels, foxes, bobcats, and even bears may be seen hunting their prey. White-tailed deer may pass by, browsing on the small plants or lower leaves of the trees. And everywhere there are insects, flying in the air, burrowing in the ground, feeding and crawling on leaves and branches, even digging into plants and animals. All these different animals would not be visible at one time, or in one part of the forest, but would be encountered as we got to know the particular forest well.

At first this complex community of living things seems chaotic. As we watch, however, certain patterns begin to emerge. Most of the animals confine their activities to limited parts of the forest.

The insects and related small animals are most noticeably confined by these limits. Many of them are found only in the soil or in the litter on the ground. Others are found only in the small plants and bushes. Still others live on the trunks of the trees, or in their upper branches and leaves.

We can think of the forest as divided into layers, or *strata*. The leaves and branches of the tall trees make up the upper stratum. Beneath this is the lower tree stratum. A shrub layer rises to about 10 feet above the ground. The ground layer, or field layer, is made up of the small plants rising only a few inches above the ground. A subterranean layer is below the ground surface. This stratum contains not only plant roots, but most of the plant body of fungi. (*Fungi* are the group of nongreen plants that includes the mushrooms and molds.) Tree trunks and rock surfaces may show the scaly growths called *lichens*.

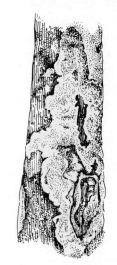

The Address of an Organism

Preferences for certain strata make it possible for different kinds of animals to live peacefully as neighbors without

Figure 2–4
The red-eyed vireo (left) and the hooded warbler (right) find their insect food supply in different strata, so they are able to live peacefully in the same forest.

competition. For example, among birds, both red-eyed vireos and hooded warblers feed upon all kinds of insects, including caterpillars, beetles, ants, flies, and locusts. Yet the vireos hunt their food in the treetop canopy, while the hooded warblers hunt on the ground layer. Thus both kinds of bird live in the same forest, without crowding each other out in the struggle for food.

There are other ways in which animals may share the forest, however. For example, in Wisconsin, scarlet tanagers hunt insects among the drier woods of south-facing slopes, while wood thrushes, also insect-eaters, hunt in the moister groves of north-facing slopes. In New York, pines and spruce have been planted over large areas to restore the forests cut down by man. Green warblers are found chiefly in the pine forests, while magnolia warblers and Nashville warblers live in the spruce trees.

Each organism is found in a certain kind of locality. This place where an organism lives is called its *habitat*. In a sense, the habitat is the "address" of the organism—the place where you would go to look for it.

The habitat of a plant seems to be determined chiefly by the soil, temperature, moisture, and light conditions.

The habitat of an animal depends partly on these factors, but also upon the presence of the plants and animals that provide its food and shelter.

Ruffed grouse

The habitat of blue grouse and spruce grouse is the coniferous forest. These birds feed largely on the needles of conifers in the northern forests. The ruffed grouse feeds in a mixed pine–hardwood forest habitat, eating a variety of leaves, twigs, and buds. The sage grouse feeds almost entirely upon the leaves and flowers of the sage-brush. Because of the way the sage grouse is colored, it is well hidden in the sage, and its nesting habits are adapted to this particular plant. Thus the habitat of the sage grouse is sharply restricted to places where sagebrush grows.

Insects often have very limited habitats. A particular kind of beetle may live only in the bark or leaves of a single kind of plant.

Whenever two kinds of plants or animals live in the same habitat and compete for the *same* source of food or energy, one will eventually crowd the other out. One of the competing kinds of organisms may be more efficient at taking advantage of what the habitat has to offer than the other is. It will feed better, reproduce better, survive

Sage grouse

harsh conditions more often, and thus come to dominate and then monopolize the habitat. Contrary to old-fashioned ideas, there seldom is any bloody struggle for survival going on. One kind of organism is better adapted to the habitat than another. Its advantage may be slight, but in the course of time, this advantage will count.

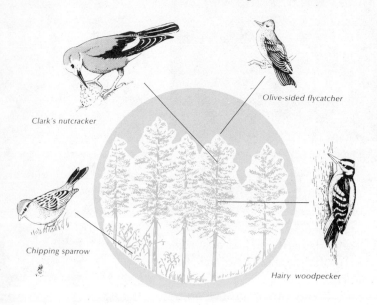

Clark's nutcracker

Olive-sided flycatcher

Chipping sparrow

Hairy woodpecker

Figure 2–5
The four birds shown each obtain their food supply from a different stratum of the Douglas fir tree. In other words, like the vireo and warbler, they have different "addresses," or habitats.

An Organism's Occupation

Yet there are cases where two different kinds of animal do occupy the same habitat without competition. For example, both moles and prairie dogs burrow in the soil. Yet they do not compete, because the mole feeds upon worms and insects, while the prairie dog lives on plant roots and bulbs. Although these two animals live in the same habitat, they play very different roles in the community. We say that they occupy different *niches*.

The niche an organism fills is what it does in the community, and so reflects its relationship to the other organisms. The source of energy, the food supply of the organism, is the most important factor in determining its niche. In human terms, we could say that an organism's habitat is its address, while its niche is its job or occupation in the community.

In general, we may say that two different kinds of organisms cannot long occupy exactly the same habitat and niche. In their competition for food and space, sooner or later one will crowd out the other. Again, the one that wins out is the one that is more efficient at taking advantage of what the niche has to offer. The other may remain in the habitat, but in another niche.

Figure 2–6

Although the mole (top) and the prairie dog both occupy the same habitat, they have different niches, or "occupations," in that habitat. What do these two animals eat?

This idea was first developed through some laboratory experiments. When two different kinds of bacteria were placed in a tube with a supply of food, the kind that reproduced fastest would thrive, while the other kind died out. In one such experiment, however, both kinds of bacteria thrived. In this case it turned out tnat one kind of bacteria fed on the food that settled to the bottom, while the other kind fed on food suspended in the liquid. These two populations occupied different habitats, and thus were able to survive although they fed on the same kind of food. Other experiments showed that bacteria could survive in the same living space—the same habitat—if they used different kinds of food. In this case they did not compete because they occupied different niches within the same habitat.

There is a saying among ecologists that "niches tend to become filled." If a possible niche exists and no organism is present to fill it, then in time some species in the habitat may gradually adapt to fill it. If an empty niche exists, and so does a niche filler, but the latter is absent locally, it may eventually migrate in. For example, if conditions in your garden are good for a certain weed, and seeds of that weed are brought in by the wind or by a bird, you will notice the filling of a niche that you had not known was there.

Competition is not the only relationship that may exist between populations of different kinds of organisms in a community. In some cases two different organisms may be of benefit to each other. For example, certain kinds of fungi grow on the roots of conifer trees. These fungi draw nutriment-rich fluids from the tree roots for their food. However, they also help to draw water and minerals from the soil into the roots. The presence of the fungi makes it possible for the conifers to grow in soil that would otherwise be too dry or too barren of minerals for their survival.

Such a relationship of mutual benefit is called *mutualism*. A striking case of mutualism between a plant and an animal is found in the desert of the Southwest. The yucca plant is fertilized only by the female yucca moth, which carries pollen from one plant to another. The moth does this as she lays her eggs in the developing seed pods of the plant. When the eggs hatch, the moth larvae eat some, but not all, of the yucca seeds. The relationship leads to the feeding of the moth larvae and the fertilization of the plants. Neither organism could survive without the other.

Figure 2–7

How is the pollination of the yucca plant by the yucca moth of mutual benefit to both organisms?

   In some cases, one organism benefits from a relationship, while the other is neither helped nor harmed. This is called *commensalism*. Many examples are found at the seashore, in relationships between immobile sea plants or animals and hard-shelled moving animals. Certain hermit crabs actually attach certain sea anemones, which are immobile animals, to their shells. The crab seems to gain some camouflage, but the anemone, which catches in its many tentacles any small animals that blunder into them, could just as well be attached to a rock. It is not harmed by living on the crab, but probably not benefited either.

In the open sea, there are certain barnacles that live on the jawbones of whales. The barnacles—which, like sea anemones, must be attached somewhere—have a safe place of attachment and a steady food supply. The whale may gain nothing from this but is not harmed.

Figure 2–8

A sea anemone shown attached to the shell of a hermit crab. How does this commensalism differ from the relationship called mutualism?

It is a short step from commensalism to *parasitism*. In this case one organism benefits at the expense of the other organism, called the *host*, with which it lives. A parasite draws nourishment from its host, weakening the host, but not killing it—at least not rapidly. Both plants and animals are attacked by parasites, and both plants and animals may be parasites.

Parasites may live inside or outside their hosts. They may be able to move from host to host, as dog fleas do. Or they may spend their adult lives attached to a single host, as a tapeworm does.

Almost everything in the forest supports a number of parasites, and some of those have even smaller parasites. The romantic mistletoe festooning oak tree branches is a parasite feeding on the tree. A tick on a rabbit is also a parasite, feeding on the rabbit's blood. Such things as ticks and fleas may also have internal parasites, even smaller than they are.

Finally, there is the relationship of *predation*, where one organism kills another and consumes all or part of it. It is difficult to draw a line between predation and parasitism. For example, certain wasps lay their eggs on living spiders, which they paralyze but do not kill with their sting. The larvae that hatch from the eggs feed on the tissues of the helpless spider. Is the growing wasp larva a parasite on the spider, or a predator that acts slowly— since the spider is eventually eaten to death, and all but completely consumed?

The relations between predators and prey are complex. A predator may even be beneficial to the prey species, weeding out the weak and sick members. This conserves the prey species' food supply, or may help to keep a disease from spreading. Predation and competition play extremely important roles in any ecosystem.

Figure 2–9

The mud wasp stores partially paralyzed spiders in her mud home for later use as food by the young. Is the wasp a parasite or a predator on the spiders?

Feeding Levels

Let us look now at another way the forest ecosystem functions. This time let us follow the movement of energy through the system along the food chains of predator-prey relationships. Energy arrives in the ecosystem in the form of sunlight. This solar energy is trapped by the leaves of the trees and other green plants. Through the process of photosynthesis, they use the energy to produce their plant tissues from water and carbon dioxide, and from minerals drawn from the soil. Some of the energy is stored within the complex molecules of the plant tissue. As we have said, these plants are the producers of the system. No other organisms can make direct use of the sunlight and inorganic materials in this way.

Many kinds of animal feed upon the plants. Birds eat seeds, buds, and foliage. Insects of various kinds eat all parts of the plants. Deer and rabbits eat twigs and leaves. Gophers attack the roots. These plant eaters are the primary consumers of the system. They are also called *herbivores*, which simply means "plant eaters." The energy they need for their life processes, plus the materials they need for body-building, are stored in the tissues of the plants that they eat.

These herbivores in turn may be eaten by secondary consumers, or *carnivores*—their name simply means "meat eaters." These include hawks, owls, foxes, insect-eating birds and shrews, skunks, snakes, and many insects that eat other insects. Scavengers, of course, may also feed at this level.

Some carnivores may feed on other carnivores, though this happens in the sea more frequently than on land. Examples in the forest would be hawks that eat snakes and weasels among their other prey. Such hawks would be tertiary consumers.

Even higher feeding levels are possible. As we shall see later, they are rare in nature, especially on land, though of course a scavenger that eats a dead hawk is eating at a higher level for the moment.

Not all organisms can be located precisely at a single feeding level. Some animals are *omnivores*—that is, they can feed on plant or animal tissue (and the name means, roughly, "everything-eaters"). The eastern red fox, for example, does not limit its diet to mice, rabbits, birds, lizards, and other small animals. Fruits and seeds make up about one fourth of its diet in summer and fall. Bears are technically carnivores, classed that way along with wolves and dogs, mountain lions and cats, and other meat-eaters. Bears eat many small mammals, snakes, and even fish. But a large part of a bear's diet is grasses, berries, fruits, leaves, and bark. In practice, bears are omnivores—and so are men.

Figure 2–10
Although bears are meat-eaters, a large part of their diet is plant material, just as it is with man. The grizzly and her cub shown were photographed in the interior of Alaska in August.

At the final feeding level are, of course, the decomposers. These are for the most part microscopic, such as bacteria and yeasts. Decomposers break up the complex molecules of dead plant and animal tissue and waste matter into simpler forms that can be used again by the producers.

An important thing to remember about the decomposers is that they can help recycle only matter, not energy. As plants, animals, and decomposers use energy, they convert it into heat, most of which is eventually radiated away into space.

Almost every ecosystem contains at least two levels of consumers. Any organism is potential prey for the organisms of the feeding level above it. Any organism is a potential competitor of the organisms at the same feeding level. With these concepts established, we can begin to study and measure the relationships in any ecosystem, not just the forest. A pond, an ocean, a coral atoll, a desert, or a grassy prairie will all have their feeding levels, their varied niches, and their relationships of competition, mutualism, parasitism, and predation.

Test Yourself

1. What is a coniferous forest?
2. What is a hardwood, or deciduous, forest?
3. What is the distinction between a habitat and a niche? (Give an example of each.)
4. Distinguish between mutualism, commensalism, and parasitism. (Give examples.)
5. Why is man called an omnivore?
6. Does man have other relationships than predation with other organisms? Can you give examples?
7. Write a description of an aquarium or fishbowl as an ecosystem. Identify feeding levels, niches, and habitats of the various organisms in the ecosystem. As far as you can, describe any competition, predation, commensalism, mutualism, or parasitism that may exist in the ecosystem.
8. Discuss the following statement: Most diseases are instances or cases of parasitism.

3

The Food Web

Interlinked Food Chains

In the preceding chapters we became acquainted with the ideas of food chains and feeding levels. We also considered some basic relationships between organisms, and a little about matter and energy. Now we are about to look at what happens to matter and energy in a total ecosystem and develop some feel for efficiency in various systems. It is important to know not only what goes through a system, but how much. So there is yet more to this topic of food.

The food chain is a useful concept in sorting out the relationships between creatures in an ecosystem. It is a simple way of showing which organisms feed upon which others. Suppose we look at one common food chain. Grasshoppers feed upon the leaves of plants. Chipping sparrows make their meals of grasshoppers. The Cooper hawk catches and eats chipping sparrows. We can diagram this food chain:

plant leaves → grasshoppers → chipping sparrows
→ Cooper hawk

This diagram shows the feeding levels running from producer to tertiary consumer.

But this is not the only food chain that could be drawn. Other insects, such as beetles, flies, caterpillars, and moths also feed upon the plants. So do many mammals and small birds. Grasshoppers are food for many kinds of birds, and for foxes, raccoons, opossums, skunks, mice, and other small mammals, and even for some other insects. The sparrows provide food for other hunting birds, for foxes and other small mammals, and even for some reptiles such as snakes. We could diagram many food chains—and find them crossing and intertwining. In doing this, we develop a complicated *food web*.

Figure 3–1

Is this diagram of a simple food chain a complete representation of what actually happens in nature?

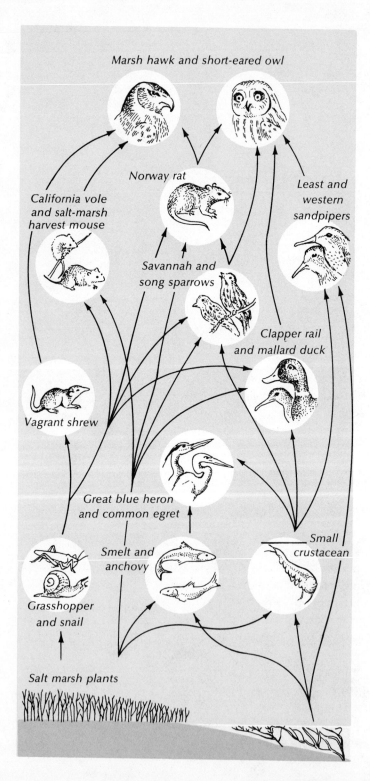

Figure 3–2

A simplified diagram of the food web in a salt marsh in the San Francisco Bay area in mid-winter.

Food webs, made of many interlinked food chains, are typical of most natural ecosystems. Figure 3-2 shows a simplified food web traced during the study of a salt marsh.

As you trace the food chains within the web, you will see that some animals occupy different feeding levels in different chains. The sparrows, for example, feed both upon seeds of the marsh grasses and upon grasshoppers and small marine animals. Thus they are both primary and secondary consumers. However, it is clear that the plants belong at the bottom of the web and the hawks and owls at the top. The other organisms can be grouped more or less exactly at levels in between.

As you look at any chain within this web, you may notice a common fact among nearly all of them. The animals generally grow larger as we move up the chain. It is less obvious, but still noticeable, that there are *fewer* of each kind of animal in the area as we go up the chain.

One sparrow eats many grasshoppers. The number of sparrows that can live in an area is considerably smaller than the number of grasshoppers. In turn, each hawk must be able to hunt over an area that contains many sparrows.

We can begin to understand these relationships when we look at the flow of energy through the food web. All energy used by the community of plants and animals comes originally from the sun. Only the plants—the producers—can capture and use solar energy in the process of photosynthesis. The size and complexity of the animal community is obviously limited by the amount of plant material produced.

By measuring or estimating the total mass of living organisms (the *biomass*) at each level in a food web, we can get some idea of the way energy moves through the system.

Plant Production in Food Webs

As you would expect, the amount of plant material produced in a year varies greatly from place to place. In a high mountain meadow, plants are small, widely scat-

Figure 3–3
Plant production—the making of food by photosynthesis—in a cornfield can be 13,000 times that in a high meadow.

tered, and grow very slowly. Only a pound or two of material is produced on an acre in a year. In contrast, an area covered by shrubs may produce 1800 pounds of plant material per acre in a year. Fields tended by man usually have high rates of production. Measurements on a corn field in Wisconsin showed that more than 13,000 pounds per acre were produced in a year, and this did not count the weeds.

In a forest, there is a huge amount of plant matter at any one time. The tree trunks alone, in a thick forest, make up about 200,000 pounds or more per acre. And the amount added each year is about 7,000 to 20,000 pounds per acre.

The highest rates of plant production seem to be in the water. Coral reefs in warm oceans are regions of very rapid plant growth. Here more than 70,000 pounds of plant matter per acre may be produced in a year.

Even these very high production rates represent only a small part of the energy available from the sun. About 1 to 3 percent of the solar energy received by a forest or field is stored in plant matter. The highest growth rates measured show a use of about 9 percent of the solar

energy. And this was only for a period of a few weeks when plants were growing most rapidly.

What happens to the plant material produced? Again, measurements help us to see where the energy goes.

A study of a salt marsh showed that less than 10 percent of the plant material was eaten by primary consumers. About 45 percent was washed out of the marsh by tides and river currents. The remaining 45 percent settled to the bottom as the plants died, where it was eaten by the decomposers.

A study in a European deciduous forest showed that only about 7 percent of the year's leaf crop was eaten by insects. The rest fell to the forest floor in the fall and went to the decomposers.

Apparently the herbivores consume only a small part of the plant matter produced. Not all that they do eat becomes new animal tissue. Much is not used at all, but is passed through the body and eliminated in the droppings, or feces. Of the food absorbed, much is used to produce energy to keep the animal going. Energy is used in moving about, digesting food, and in replacing the normal wear and tear of the body. Only the small part of energy that is left over can be used to produce new body tissues.

The Food Web
as a Pyramid

It would appear, then, that only a tiny fraction of the plant material produced each year is turned into new animal matter. In a similar way, only a small fraction of the new mass of herbivores is turned into new carnivore mass.

A rough idea of this effect can be gained simply by counting the number of organisms in an area. A study of a bluegrass field produced the following results:

Kind of organism	Number of organisms
birds and moles	3
spiders, ants, carnivorous beetles, etc.	354,904
plant-eating insects, etc.	708,624
green plants	5,842,424

As you can see, a tremendous number of producers are able to support only three tertiary consumers at the top of the food web. This "pyramid of numbers" is shown as a diagram in Figure 3-4.

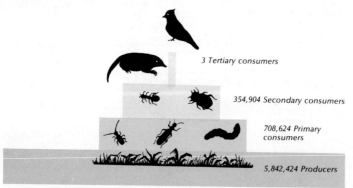

3 Tertiary consumers

354,904 Secondary consumers

708,624 Primary consumers

5,842,424 Producers

Figure 3-4

An example of the "pyramid of numbers," obtained by counting the number of organisms in a bluegrass field.

However, you may recall that the organisms at the higher levels of the food web are generally larger. One bird or mole contains as much animal tissue as a large number of the insects that it eats. And what about the energy? A more realistic idea of the energy used in living matter at each level would come from a measure of the biomass at each level. This is, of course, much more difficult to obtain than a simple count of organisms (which is difficult enough in itself). Some estimates have been made, however. The results show that the "pyramid of mass" is almost as striking as the "pyramid of numbers."

One study was made in a water habitat, the spring community at Silver Springs, Florida. Here the principal producers are beds of eelgrass and the *algae* (smaller, more primitive green plants) that grow on them. Water insects, snails, fish, and turtles are primary consumers. Secondary consumers are various fish and insects which feed on the herbivores. At the top of the food web are the large fish, bass and gar, which feed chiefly on secondary consumers. The mass of fungi and bacteria that act as decomposers was measured in this study also. The results are shown in the following table and in Figure 3-5.

Feeding Level	Biomass (pounds per acre)
Tertiary consumers	13
Secondary consumers	98
Primary consumers	327
Producers (plants)	7225
Decomposers	44

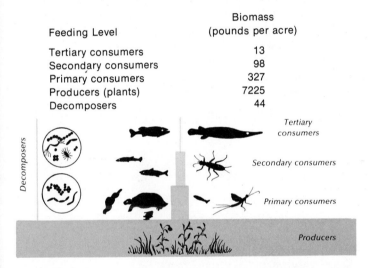

Tertiary consumers

Secondary consumers

Primary consumers

Producers

Decomposers

Figure 3-5

A "pyramid of mass," showing the relative mass per acre of organisms at various feeding levels at Silver Springs, Florida.

This was an unusually productive ecosystem. The plants here produce about 57,000 pounds of plant matter per acre each year. As you can see, this means that the total mass of plants existing at any one time is only a small part of the mass produced in a year. New plants grow and die rapidly, and are constantly being browsed by herbivores.

We can say that the spring has a relatively small mass of plants at any one time (*standing crop*), but a rapid rate at which plants die and are replaced by new plants (*turnover rate*). In a forest, the situation is quite different. Much of the plant mass is in the slowly growing tree trunks. The standing crop is much larger than the annual turnover. Thus, even the measurements of biomass may not give an accurate idea of the production rate, or of energy used at each level.

For example, the mass of decomposers in the Silver Springs pyramid is very small. Yet these tiny organisms use as much or more energy in a year as do the primary consumers. Although there is not a very great mass of decomposers at any one time, they have a very high turn-over rate. They live only a short time, and the entire mass of decomposers may be replaced every few weeks or even days by new organisms.

Your common sense would suggest that a larger organism, such as a bird, needs more energy for living than does a smaller one, such as a grasshopper. This is correct. It is one reason why so few large organisms are found at the top of a food pyramid containing thousands of times as many plants, or a much greater biomass of plants. It explains why not all the food an animal eats is converted into animal tissue and thus into biomass. The major part of the food consumed supplies energy for life activities.

Man's Position in the Food Web

Man is an omnivore. He can survive on either plants or animals, or on both. Thus, by varying his diet, he can choose his place in a food web. He can also shift his level on a food pyramid upward or downward to some extent.

Let us suppose that a man chooses to live entirely on meat. In order to supply enough beef for his needs, he would need to maintain a steady herd of about seven to ten cattle. These in turn would require about ten acres of cultivated alfalfa for their feed.

On the other hand, suppose that he chooses to live entirely on wheat. In this case, he might raise enough food to support himself on less than half an acre, given good soil, adequate moisture delivered at the proper times, not too much competition from insects, and some luck.

By converting himself from a secondary to a primary consumer, man is able to increase the efficiency of his use of solar energy. A great deal of energy is lost in the extra link of the plant→beef→man chain. However, people would suffer considerable malnutrition from a wheat-only diet.

The main problem with an exclusive wheat diet is lack of protein. Wheat and other cereal grains do contain some protein. But cereals do not contain what are known as *complete proteins*, which supply all human protein needs. A person living on an exclusive wheat diet would suffer from protein-deficiency diseases.

Complete proteins can be obtained from many nuts, though not in the same concentrations or quality as in animal sources. Certain mixtures of cereal grains and seeds of the *legume* family (which includes peas, beans, peanuts, and soybeans) can also supply complete proteins. However, obtaining complete protein through a diet consisting entirely of plant products requires considerable knowledge and planning, as well as the availability of a variety of the products.

Still, a large amount of animal protein in the human diet is a luxury. Most peoples of the world today do not have this luxury. In countries such as the United States, we can afford to use a great deal of land for the raising of meat animals. The average American gets more than one third of his food energy from animal products, including milk and eggs.

In Asia, where the amount of available farmland per person is much smaller, the luxury of a longer food chain cannot be afforded. In India, for example, even if every bit of land could be farmed, there would be less than 1.5 acres of farmland per person. But not all the land can be farmed, and much of that which can be has badly depleted soils. In these countries, a vegetarian diet is necessary. Deficiency diseases are common and infant and childhood mortality rates are high.

The Impact of Hunting and Agriculture in Man's History

Most students of man's early history think that he learned early to depend heavily on meat. Once man had tools and weapons, he could kill fairly large animals and tap the large store of nutrients and energy concentrated in their flesh. This really was an increase in feeding efficiency over continuous browsing on plant matter—fruits, nuts, seeds, berries, roots—and probably insects and grubs. The hunting man could keep more of his children alive, support a larger family. But man remained an omnivore. Like bears and other large predators, man supplemented his meat diet with plant foods. Still, early man probably received more than half his energy from animal foods whenever he could obtain them. This situation existed for hundreds of thousands of years.

At some time, less than ten thousand years ago, man learned to cultivate crops and domesticate animals. He was able to concentrate his food supply in a much smaller area of land, and to spend much less energy in chasing after food. As a result, the human population could become much larger. By domestication, man was able to provide ahead for food. Death rates went down as starvation was less frequent during harsh seasons. Also, since not every person in a group was needed just for the gathering of food, division of labor became possible, and certain advantages were gained. Art, poetry, religion, and even technology and science could be explored and developed, now that men could settle down in definite homesites. This led to invention after invention that made even larger numbers of human beings possible.

Today the human population has become so large that the old way of life as a secondary consumer may be in danger. The biomass of human beings is becoming so large that our species may be required to support itself at the primary consumer level. This, as we have seen, has disadvantages. It may not really be possible.

There have been many other effects of man's change in life style. As he farmed the land with crops that were good food for him, he weeded out plants that were at the bottom of other food chains. To protect his new fields, he killed many other primary consumers that attempted to eat the plants. To protect his herds and flocks, he also killed many of the other carnivores. The changes in the food webs have been widespread, and are still going on.

Very early, once agriculture had been developed, man began to exhaust farmland by several harmful practices. Repeated plantings and harvests of a single kind of crop plant can remove key nutrients from the soil, so that eventually that crop cannot grow. Often no other desired crop can grow either. Such practices continued in our own country right into this century. Only recently has *crop rotation* become widespread. This is the practice of planting fields to clover and other legumes, which restore certain essential nutrients to the soil, every two or three seasons. Later, the field can be used as a pasture, and later still, for the grain crop again. Also, soils must have dead plant tissue in order to have the texture that lets in water and air and to keep the complex communities of decomposers alive. Finally, animal manures can return many needed nutrient minerals to soil. Only in the past couple of centuries has the necessity for applying manure or other fertilizers to fields been widely appreciated. In many countries of the world, this still is not commonly done.

When the human population was much smaller, entire nations could move once they had exhausted their soils and find new soils. Moving on when the soil could produce no more crops was the custom for many farmers in the United States right into this century. This was one driving factor in the settlement of the country all the way to the Pacific Coast. But nowadays there is no more land waiting for settlement.

Until recently, man was unaware of the effects of his actions on the food web. Today, we are becoming concerned about these effects and their possible results for man. We are also beginning to think about ways to make changes in our own food chain for our benefit.

There are many problems to be considered. We still know very little about the decomposers of our food web.

Do our activities harm them? Can we help them be more efficient? Is there any way that the productivity of the producers can be increased beyond about 3 percent of the available solar energy? Can the upper levels of the pyramid be broadened without a larger base level? What happens to the biomass of the various levels when the ecosystem is simplified? This occurs when there are fewer different kinds of organisms at each level, as in farming, where a single kind of plant makes up the entire producer level.

We will return to these problems in later chapters. In the meantime, you should already know enough to make some good guesses about possible answers.

Test Yourself

1. Why have food webs replaced food chains in this chapter's discussion?
2. Why do ecologists speak of food pyramids? What things are involved in them? What do these pyramids show?
3. What is biomass?
4. What would be an advantage to man's living on one plant crop exclusively (or even just a few plant crops)?
5. What are the disadvantages for man of trying to live on one plant crop?
6. What is crop rotation? What does it accomplish?
7. In physics, the second law of thermodynamics states that some energy is always lost whenever stored energy is changed from one form to another. Scientists call this a law because it happens unavoidably. How is this law related to observations we have made about the food web or pyramid?

8. An ancient Chinese proverb states that "each hill has only one tiger." Explain this saying in terms of what you have learned about the nature of food pyramids.
9. Explain how domestication of plants and animals made larger human populations possible.
10. What are the two main reasons why all the food eaten by organisms at one feeding level is not turned into body substance, or *biomass*, at that level?

4

The Limits of the Environment

Limiting Factors

We have seen that each kind of organism occupies a certain kind of environment. Some organisms are very narrow in their preferences. A particular bird may always be found nesting or feeding in a certain kind of tree. Others travel widely, visiting many different habitats.

What factors determine the spread of a particular kind of organism? Why don't all plants and animals spread out over all the available space?

Clearly, an organism is limited by its own physical needs. A trout cannot survive out of the water. A human being cannot survive out of the air. The water surface is obviously an important barrier to the spread of these and many other species.

In a similar way, factors such as temperature or availability of light may limit the distribution of a species. A plant that is killed by freezing temperatures will not be able to gain a foothold in the far north. A plant that requires a great deal of water will not be found out in the desert.

We can see that an organism with a high degree of tolerance for all of these factors will probably be widespread. If an organism requires a particular condition for its survival, it may be very narrow in its *range* (the area over which it is found). For example, if a plant needs a great deal of light to survive, it will not be found in shady areas, even though the other conditions (moisture, temperature, soil, etc.) might be well within its limits of tolerance. In other places, the light may be perfect, but lack of water prevents the plant from surviving.

Thus, the *limiting factor* in one part of the range may be different from that in another part. For many North American plants, the northern border of the range is determined by cold winter temperatures, while the southern border is determined by the availability of water. To become established in any spot, a plant must be able to reproduce, to produce seeds. Length of day and even length of night govern the flowering and seeding schedules of many plants. Day and night lengths depend on latitude—on how far north or south a location is.

In fact, the interactions are often even more complicated. As one factor approaches the organism's limit of tolerance, its tolerance for other factors may be decreased. For example, grass may grow in soil that contains just barely enough nitrogen to supply the needs of the plant. However, under these conditions grass is much more sensitive than normal to shortages of water. A drought that would not seriously harm grass in a nitrogen-rich soil will kill the grass in nitrogen-poor soil.

A very important factor in determining the range of plants is the availability of minerals and nutrient chemicals in the soil. Some 30 to 40 of the basic chemical elements are needed for the growth and development of a living organism. However, most organisms need at least some of these elements in particular chemical compounds. That is, a pure element like hydrogen would not be usable. It has to be supplied at least by water (which has two hydrogen atoms and one oxygen atom in its molecule). Carbon, nitrogen, and most of the other necessary elements must also appear as compounds. Most of the compounds needed are originally produced by other organisms. Most of these materials move from the nonliving part of the ecosystem into the bodies of organisms, and eventually back into the nonliving environment again.

The Nitrogen Cycle

One vital element that cycles in this way is nitrogen. It plays an important part in the structure of all organisms because it is essential to the making of proteins. There is plenty of nitrogen around; it makes up about 78 percent of the atmosphere. However, plants are not able to use pure nitrogen gas in building their tissues. Most green plants need nitrogen in the form of nitrates: compounds of nitrogen, oxygen, and at least one other element. Plants absorb these nitrates from the soil through their roots and use them in making the more complicated chemicals of plant tissue.

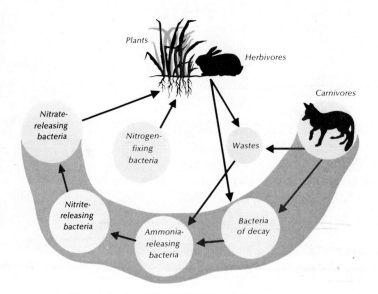

Plants

Herbivores

Carnivores

Nitrate-releasing bacteria

Nitrogen-fixing bacteria

Wastes

Nitrite-releasing bacteria

Ammonia-releasing bacteria

Bacteria of decay

Figure 4–1

A diagramatic representation of the nitrogen cycle.

The plants may be eaten by herbivores, and they in turn by carnivores. At each step, the complex nitrogen compounds are used in building new living tissues. Some nitrogen is released in various waste products excreted by living organisms. These waste chemicals (such as urea, found in urine and sweat) and the tissues of dead plants and animals are broken down by the decomposers. The first step in decomposition is carried out by decay bacteria, which break complex compounds such as proteins down into chemicals called amino acids. Another group of bacteria consume some of these compounds and release ammonia (a compound of nitrogen and hydrogen). The ammonia is taken in by still another kind of bacteria, and excreted in the form of chemicals called nitrites. Finally, yet another group of bacteria turn the nitrites into nitrates. When these are released into the soil, they can again be picked up by plant roots.

The main parts of the nitrogen cycle are shown in Figure 4-1. There are some other complications, but they play minor parts in the cycle. For example, some nitrogen gas is turned into nitrates by the action of lightning.

The bacteria that turn nitrites into nitrates are not the only source of nitrates in the soil. Some bacteria can use the free nitrogen in the air to form nitrates as they grow. These are called *nitrogen-fixing bacteria* and they are particularly interesting. Some live free in the soil. Others are found only in nodules on the roots of certain plants. This is an excellent example of mutualism. The process has been carefully studied, and it is complex. The nodules form only on the roots of legumes. Chemicals from the legume root stimulate the growth of bacteria. Secretions from the bacteria cause the nodule to form on the root.

Figure 4–2
The nodules on the roots of this vetch plant contain nitrogen-fixing bacteria, which are able to convert free nitrogen from the air into nitrates.

The bacteria then move into the nodule. They draw certain chemicals (sugars and starches) from the plant fluids, and in turn release nitrates into the plant.

As an ecosystem exists through time, the supply of nitrates for the plants is continually refreshed by nitrogen-fixing bacteria and by the bacteria which break down waste products. When man moves in to simplify an ecosystem for his own purposes, the cycle may be broken. All of the legume plants may be cleared out in order to plant wheat or other crops. The animals are chased out of the field or killed, and then nitrogen-bearing waste products are lost to the soil. Harvesting the crop removes the major part of the plant material from the field. This plant material contains nitrogen compounds that came from the soil.

With the supply of waste products removed, the decay bacteria cease to supply nitrates. The nitrogen-fixing bacteria are greatly decreased in number with the removal of the legumes. Only the free-living bacteria remain. As each generation of crop plants is grown and removed, the amount of nitrates in the soil decreases. After a few years, the nitrogen level drops below the limit of tolerance of the wheat or other crop. The wheat plants become smaller and sparser with each crop, and finally will not grow at all.

Long before the nitrogen cycle was known, farmers discovered that certain steps could be taken to keep their soil in condition. As much as possible of the unused part of the plants should be plowed back into the field. Waste materials such as sewage and manure should be spread over the land. Farmers also found it helpful to raise a crop of legumes on plots of land every two or three years in place of the usual crops of other plants. This is the familiar practice of crop rotation.

Today fertilizers containing nitrates and other chemicals necessary to plant growth are prepared in chemical factories. The heavy use of fertilizers plays an important part in the high productivity of farms in northern Europe and Japan, as well as the United States. Heavy use of commercial fertilizers can have ecological disadvantages, however, as we shall see later.

Oxygen, Carbon, and Trace Elements in the Environment

Similar cycles exist for each of the other elements used by living organisms. Among these are carbon, oxygen, hydrogen, phosphorus, potassium, calcium, magnesium, sulphur, iron, chlorine, zinc, and iodine. In most of these cycles, the unseen decomposers play very important roles. The details of some cycles are still being worked out.

Each of the necessary elements must be present in the proper amounts if an organism is to survive. The availability of these elements is an important limiting factor to the range of an organism. Oxygen, carbon, and nitrogen are the elements that make up the major portion by weight of animal tissue. They are needed in large quantities by any living organism.

Both plants and animals need oxygen gas for *respiration;* that is, for burning food chemicals to get energy. Oxygen is given off by green plants in the food-making process we have identified as photosynthesis. This is the major source of oxygen in the atmosphere. Oxygen is usually available in adequate amounts in land environments. It becomes scarce only at high altitudes (where the atmosphere is thin), deep in the ground, or in water-soaked soil.

Water organisms make use of the oxygen dissolved in the water. Some of this oxygen is absorbed from the air; some is released by plants growing in the water. The amount of oxygen dissolved in water varies greatly with the temperature and depth of the water. (Warmer water has a lower capacity for dissolved oxygen than colder water.) The amount of oxygen in the water limits the range of water organisms in many cases.

Plants obtain carbon from the gas carbon dioxide, which they absorb in the process of photosynthesis. This gas makes up only about 0.03 percent of the atmosphere, and its concentration varies from place to place. It does appear to serve as a limiting factor for plants in some cases. The productivity of plant growth is increased in

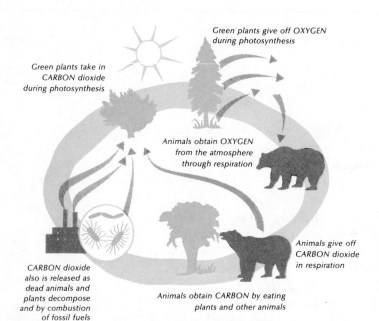

Green plants give off OXYGEN
during photosynthesis

Green plants take in
CARBON dioxide
during photosynthesis

Animals obtain OXYGEN
from the atmosphere
through respiration

Animals give off
CARBON dioxide
in respiration

CARBON dioxide
also is released as
dead animals and
plants decompose
and by combustion
of fossil fuels

Animals obtain CARBON by eating
plants and other animals

Figure 4–3

A diagramatic representation of the carbon–oxygen cycle.

many cases when they are grown in air with more carbon dioxide, as laboratory experiments have shown.

Animals obtain their supply of carbon from the plants or other animals that they eat. They are not able to make use of the carbon dioxide from the air. In fact, animals as well as plants release carbon dioxide into the air as a waste product of respiration. Much of the carbon built into plant and animal tissues is released eventually as carbon dioxide gas by the decomposers.

To summarize, we can think of a carbon–oxygen cycle rather than of each of these two elements cycling separately. The atmosphere is supplied with oxygen by green plants undergoing photosynthesis. This oxygen is in turn used by both plants and animals in respiration. A by-product of respiration is carbon dioxide, which plants in turn use to build carbon compounds during photosynthesis. These carbon compounds are obtained by animals as they eat plants, and are finally decomposed to carbon dioxide when plants and animals die.

Some elements essential to living things are needed only in very small amounts, or traces. They are commonly called *trace elements*. Cobalt is an example of a trace element. Plants do not need this element, but fortunately it is taken up into their tissues, since it is vital to all animals. Most carnivores obtain an adequate supply in the meat they eat. Grazing animals in areas where cobalt is scarce become anemic and slowly waste away. The amount needed is very small. An acre of grazing land supplies only about 0.01 ounce of cobalt per year to the animals that live on it.

Plants also need certain trace elements. For example, few plants of any kind will grow without a trace of boron in the soil. But in this case there can be too much of a good thing. If a great deal of boron is present, no plants will grow.

In an area where the soil is rich in the needed elements, all the plants and animals seem healthy. Where there are mineral deficiencies, the plants and animals throughout the food web are affected. In general, nutrients are most important as limiting factors in the ranges of plants. However, the herbivores depend on the plants for food, and the carnivores need the herbivores. Thus the absence of a single trace element may severely limit the amount of life in an area, even though all other conditions are ideal. In cases where nutrients limit the range of organisms, the use of fertilizer can often turn a barren area into a productive ecosystem.

Temperature as a Limiting Factor

Temperature is a very important limiting factor. There are certain extreme limits of temperature for living things. Few organisms can survive if the temperature of their tissues drops below freezing. Plants and animals can live in areas where temperatures drop below the freezing point only if they are able to use the heat released by use of food energy to keep their tissues warm. Animals and most plants are unable to survive for long at temperatures of more than 120°F. A few types of algae are able to live in hot springs at temperatures as high as 158°F.

Of course, these are only the extreme limits for living things. Each kind of plant or animal has its own limits of temperature tolerance. Some organisms survive only within very narrow temperature ranges. Other organisms can survive in a wide range of temperatures, but cannot endure sudden or extreme changes of temperature. Most animals and plants are unable to grow or reproduce normally at temperatures that approach their limits of tolerance, although they can survive.

Figure 4–4

In a successful adaptation to cold climates, Oregon juncos maintain a very rapid heart rate, which keeps their body temperature at about 110° F.

In areas where temperatures change greatly (from day to night, winter to summer, or sunlight to shade), animals and plants have developed many ways of keeping their own temperatures within reasonable limits. Mammals and birds use their own food energy and the circulation of their blood to keep body temperature almost constant, regardless of the air temperature. Animals use the shade of plants or burrows to avoid summer or daytime heat. Periods of extreme cold or dryness may be survived by seeds or eggs, although the adult organisms die. Some organisms are able to survive through these periods by sharply reducing their life activity until more favorable conditions return. For example, animals hibernate; many plants drop their leaves and suspend growth.

Many plants and animals are limited by the temperatures necessary for the process of reproduction. The lobster of the Atlantic Ocean, for example, can survive in ice water. However, it will not breed in water colder than about 50°F. Thus the main range of the lobster population is limited by the temperature at which it can reproduce, although wandering individuals are found in colder water.

Water and Light as Limiting Factors

Water is essential to all life. Water acts as a solvent and as a transport medium in living things, and must be present at the start of all the building processes in plant or animal cells and tissues. The moisture available in the soil, in the air, and in rainfall thus acts as a limit on plant ranges. Most animals require drinking water and can survive only where it is available.

Animals and plants adapted to life in dry regions have many ways of conserving water, or reducing their liquid-water needs. Some animals never need to drink liquid water, even if it is sometimes available. They use the waste water produced in the oxidation of their food in respira-

Figure 4–5

Shortage of water in the desert limits the kinds of organisms that can live there. The spines of cactuses are really modified leaves. Compared with typical leaves, through which a great deal of water is lost, they have relatively little surface area. The kangaroo rat does not need to drink liquid water at all.

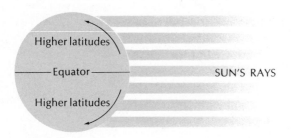

Higher latitudes

Equator

Higher latitudes

SUN'S RAYS

Figure 4–6

At latitudes near the poles, the sun's rays are spread over a wider area than they are nearer the equator. Many plants are unable to live at such latitudes because not enough light is available.

tion or in the breaking down of body fat. A classic example is the kangaroo rat of the American southwest.

The amount of sunlight available is another important limiting factor for plants. This depends on latitude: there is less sunlight available to plants in high latitudes (that is, locations far from the equator) even though summer days are very long in such latitudes. This is because of the low angle at which sunlight reaches the earth's surface at high latitudes. The available energy is spread over too wide an area. In the oceans, and even in lakes, where light penetrates only a relatively short distance into the water, plants are limited to the uppermost layers. Even in the clearest ocean water, there is not enough light for photosynthesis beyond a depth of 600 feet or so. If algae growth or silt cuts down the transparency of a lake, plant growth will be hindered not far from the surface.

So far we have been discussing mostly chemical limits for an ecosystem, but there are other considerations as well. Within any ecosystem, conditions vary from place to place, even over very short distances. Light, temperature, moisture, and soil may be quite different on a hillside from what they are in a valley, or from a north slope to a south slope. Even over distances of a few feet, conditions may change enough to produce slightly different habitats.

Each kind of organism is most abundant in the places where it finds conditions best for it. It may also exist in places where conditions are not as good, if it is not crowded out by organisms that thrive in those places. At places where conditions are outside its limits of tolerance, the organism will not be found at all.

In addition to the nonliving factors that we have discussed thus far, each organism is affected by the others. If a particular plant is needed for food or for nesting space, a bird may be limited in its range by the range of the plant. In studying the living factors of an ecosystem—the plants and animals—the ecologist, although interested in individual organisms, is more apt to group them into populations. Populations are groups of organisms of the same kind. In the next chapter we shall take a look at some of the characteristics of a population.

Test Yourself

1. Explain the meaning of limiting factors in an environment.
2. Plants need nitrogen, but cannot use the free nitrogen in the air. How do they get nitrogen?
3. What is meant by the nitrogen cycle? (Explain briefly.)
4. Where does most of the oxygen in the air come from? By what process?
5. How are bacteria in the soil and on certain plant roots important to plant and animal life?
6. When man cultivates a crop, in what main ways does he simplify the local ecosystem? What can happen as a result?
7. Why do ecologists speak of a carbon–oxygen cycle rather than of a carbon cycle and an oxygen cycle?
8. Do limiting factors operate separately, or together? Does any living thing seem to be affected by only one limiting factor? Explain.
9. In your town, are limiting factors the same for everything everywhere? Explain.
10. Can you think of any natural situations where a life community would have a sharp boundary—that is, where the limits of the ranges of all the different species would occur along the same line?
11. Compare the results of sudden freezing weather on (a) a natural ecosystem made up of many kinds of plants and animals; and (b) a field planted with only a single crop.
12. Why can man successfully raise chosen plants in fields or gardens, although those same plants may soon die out if left unattended?

5

Populations and Their Interactions

Properties of a Population

We have already used the word *population* many times. You probably have a good idea of what it means. In this chapter we shall look at the nature of populations more closely. Populations are the basic units studied by the ecologist.

A *population* is a group of organisms of the same kind living in a particular area. In Chapter 3 we looked at several ecosystems. Each contains many populations. In the salt marsh, for example, there is a population of hawks and a population of owls. There is a population of grasshoppers, a population of snails, one of shrimp, and one of marsh grasses. The ecologist is not too concerned about any particular individual organism. He is primarily interested in the various populations.

An individual organism may be sick or healthy, old or young. But when we look at the entire population, we are concerned with other properties. We look at how the population is distributed over a given space and whether it is growing or dying out. These properties represent the sum of all things that happen to the individuals. Of course the ecologist, as a scientist, is not only interested in what is happening to a population, but how it is happening. He wants to know, too, how whatever happens to one population affects other populations and the rest of the environment. As a human being, the ecologist has a vested interest in his findings: What do they mean in terms of the well being and survival of mankind?

One of the most useful properties of a population to study is its *density*. This is a measure of the number of individuals found in a given amount of space. For example, in 1970 there were about 205,000,000 human beings living in the United States. This gives a population density of about 57.5 persons per square mile. Of course, this is merely an average density for the entire country. If we consider smaller areas, the density varies greatly. In Alaska, the population density is less than one person per square mile. On New York City's Manhattan Island, there are about 75,000 people per square mile. People tend to live in clumps in certain places, while other areas are very thinly populated. The same is true for most animal and plant populations. Although the average density over a large area may be small, the density may be very great in certain favorable areas. Therefore, care must be used in choosing sample areas and in explaining how measurements were made.

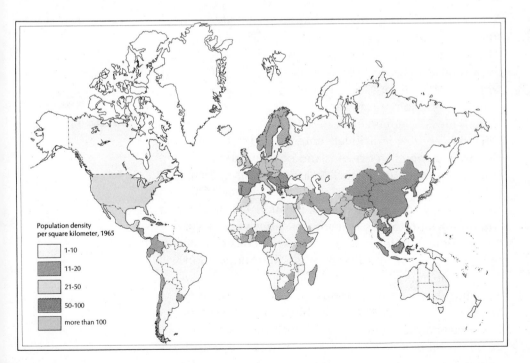

Figure 5–1
Density patterns of world population as of 1965.

As we have seen, biomass is often a more meaningful measure than numbers of individuals for comparing different kinds of organisms. If we assume that the average human weighs about 100 pounds, the average human population density of the United States could be expressed as about 5750 pounds per square mile.

The Birth Rate as a Measure of Population Change

In general, the ecologist is most interested in *changes* of population density. Within a given ecosystem, some populations may be growing, while others are declining. An understanding of these changes in populations will help us to see how and why ecosystems change or do not change over the years.

Why does a population change in size or density? Obviously, it will increase if more individuals are born than die or leave. The size of the population at any time depends upon the relationship between the rates at which new individuals arrive (through birth or immigration) and other individuals are lost (through death or emigration).

For the moment, let us consider an ecosystem that experiences a minimum of immigration and emigration. That is, very few individuals enter or leave the area that we are studying. An ocean island or a desert oasis might fill these conditions. In such a case, changes in the population depend upon the relationship between birth and death rates. Obviously, the population will increase if there are more births than deaths from year to year. It will decline if there are more deaths than births. If deaths and births occur in equal numbers, the population will remain steady.

Birth rates may be measured in several ways. For example, a population of bluebirds in a park produced 455 eggs during one year. This information would not be very useful unless we knew how many adult birds there were. In this population, there were 34 adult females. Thus, we could express the birth rate as about 13 eggs per female per year.

Of course, not all the eggs hatched, and not all the baby birds that did hatch survived long enough to leave the nest on their own. Perhaps the most useful information is the number of bluebirds that did survive to become independent members of the population. There was a total of 265 survivors for the population, or about 8 young birds per female per year.

If the number of males was about equal to the number of females, this would mean that about 4 young birds were being added to the population each year for every adult bird in the population.

The ecologist would say that this population has a *crude birth rate* of about 650 births per 100 population (1300 eggs per 100 females; 650 eggs per 100 adult birds). This population has a *specific birth rate* (birds surviving to leave the nest) of about 400 births per 100 population. The specific birth rate actually includes a part of the death rate: some organisms die before they reach some specified stage of development.

If 400 new birds are being added to the population each year for each 100 adult birds, isn't this population going to be growing very rapidly? We cannot answer that question unless we know something about the death rates. If most of those young birds and some of the older ones die during the year, the population could decline.

Determining the Death Rate

Like the birth rate, the death rate can be expressed as a simple number of deaths per 100 or 1000 individuals in the population. Comparison of birth and death rates would be enough to give us an idea of whether the population is increasing or decreasing at the moment. You can see that if the number of births exceeds the number of deaths, the population would be increasing. However, for a more complete understanding of what is happening, we need to know more about the ages of the creatures that die. Death rates are best shown by tables which indicate the number of deaths occurring each year in a group of individuals. This shows, for example, how many will be left at the end of each year of a group of 100 or 1000 individuals born at the same time. (A table of this sort is used to calculate human life expectancies in order to determine rates for life insurance.) It usually also includes a column showing the average life expectancy for an individual of a given age. This represents the number of years that an average individual of this age will survive. Table 5-1 shows such a life table for a population of black-tailed deer living in a chaparral biome.

This table gives us a great deal of information about the pattern of deaths in a deer population. Of each 1000 deer born, 372 die during the first year. About half of the

Table 5-1   Life Table for Black-Tailed Deer Living in a Chaparral Biome

Age in Years	Number Alive at Start of Interval	Number Dying During Interval	Death Rate*	Life Expectancy for this Age †
0–1	1000	372	372	4.2 years
1–2	628	41	65	5.3 years
2–3	587	66	112	4.6 years
3–4	521	68	131	4.2 years
4–5	453	67	148	3.7 years
5–6	386	54	140	3.1 years
6–7	332	54	163	2.6 years
7–8	278	54	194	2.0 years
8–9	224	33	147	1.4 years
9+	191	191	1000	0.5 years

*Number dying per 1000 population of this age group.
†At beginning of the age interval.

deer survive into their fourth year, one third survive into their seventh year, about one fifth survive into their ninth year. We can see that the death rate is quite high during the first year, then falls off sharply. The death rate increases slowly with age from the first through the eighth years, then falls slightly during the ninth year.

You may notice that a deer at birth has an average life expectancy of 4.2 years. However, if the deer manages

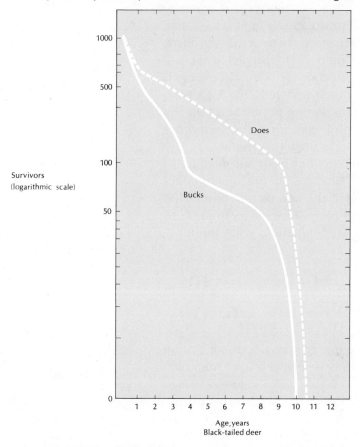

Survivors
(logarithmic scale)

Age, years
Black-tailed deer

Figure 5–2

Curves showing the number of black-tailed deer out of a population of 1000 that survive at each age. How would you explain the patterns of the two curves?

to survive through the dangerous first year, it can then expect on the average to live another 5.3 years. Such a situation is not uncommon, for there is a high death rate among the very young of many kinds of plants and animals.

This life table was constructed for the female deer. The males (bucks) have a different life expectancy, chiefly because human hunters kill many of the young bucks.

The number of animals surviving at each age can be plotted on a graph. Such a *survivorship curve* for the black-tailed deer is shown in Figure 5-2.

The survivorship curve tells at a glance a great deal about the deaths in the population. If the death rate is the same for all ages, the curve will form a straight diagonal line. If most of the creatures live a full life and die in old age, the curve will drop only slightly across the chart, then plunge suddenly near the maximum age reached by individuals. If most organisms die early in life, the curve will drop sharply at first, then more slowly across the chart.

Such a curve would help us to predict what will happen to the bluebird population we were discussing. If most bluebirds die during their first year, the high birth rate may not result in an increasing population. On the other hand, if most bluebirds live for a few years, the population is almost certain to increase rapidly.

In natural populations, neither birth nor death rates usually remain constant. Changes in the environment alter these rates and change the age distribution in the population. Careful studies may be necessary in order to find out what is actually happening and what the long-term results will be.

Characteristic Patterns of Population Growth

Maximum rates of population growth are usually found where the population density is relatively low. Abundant food and living space are available, so birth rates are high and death rates are low. Most kinds of creatures can reproduce with amazing rapidity. Some fish can produce thousands or even millions of eggs per female each year. Rats and mice produce four litters of young each year, with about six young in each litter. If given ample food, water, space, and protection from enemies, all of these offspring survive and soon begin raising young themselves. Almost any kind of organism would be capable of rapidly increasing its population to crowd the entire world within only a few dozen generations if such ideal conditions could be maintained.

Of course, this never happens. As the population increases, the death rate begins to rise. Shortages of food or shelter, overcrowding, or losses to predators and disease begin to kill more and more of the population. The same conditions make the females less healthy, and the birth rate begins to decrease.

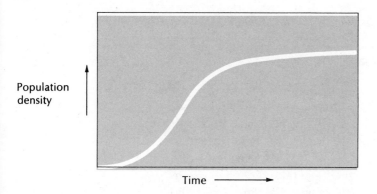

Population density

Time

Figure 5–3

A typical population curve in which growth begins slowly, then becomes rapid as more and more parents appear, and finally levels off as further growth is limited by the environment.

As a result, a graph showing the population density over a long period of time often takes the S-shaped form shown in Figure 5-3. Population growth is slow at first, because there are few organisms reproducing. The rate becomes ever more rapid (the curve becoming steeper) as each generation brings a larger and larger number of parents. Then the curve levels off as the environment fails to sustain the rate of increase.

As an example, let us suppose that we begin with a pair of rabbits. We shall simplify matters by assuming that each pair of rabbits produces four young during a year, and that these are ready to become parents in the following year. For the moment, we shall assume that none of the rabbits dies or becomes too old to reproduce.

The first year, the initial pair of rabbits produces four young. The next year, there will be six rabbits (three pairs) which will produce 12 young. In the third year, there will be 18 rabbits (9 pairs) which will produce 36 young. Table 5-2 shows the resulting population growth. Even if we allowed for the fact that the rabbits would grow old and die after a few years of breeding, we would still obtain a curve of population growth much like that in the first part of Figure 5-3.

Table 5-2   Growth of a Hypothetical Population of Rabbits

Year	Rabbit Pairs at Beginning of Year	Number of Young Produced	Population at Beginning of Following Year
1	1	4	6
2	3	12	18
3	9	36	54
4	27	108	162
5	81	324	486
6	243	972	1458
7	729	2916	4374
8	2187	8748	13,122
9	6561	26,244	39,366
10	19,683	78,732	118,098
		and so on . . .	

It is clear that this population growth could not continue for very long. As the density increases, the death rate begins to rise. Starvation, disease, or fighting lead to the deaths of more and more rabbits. The overcrowded conditions may also cause the birth rate to decline. Eventually, if the birth rate and death rate become equal, the population density may become stable at some level, as shown in the graph.

Growth curves such as this can be observed in laboratory experiments. When a small population is placed in a well-supplied environment, the curve may be quite similar to the simple S-shaped curve we have drawn. In nature, however, the curve does not often level out to a straight line. Instead it fluctuates in one of the forms shown in Figure 5-4.

The population density becomes so great that the carrying capacity of the environment is exceeded. Food is in shorter supply. Waste materials accumulate and may be toxic. Then deaths exceed births, and the population begins to decline. After the population has decreased a certain amount, conditions again become more favorable. The density then begins to increase, but again exceeds the optimum point, so that the fluctuations continue. These fluctuations may tend to become smaller and smaller (Figure 5-4a), so that the population approaches a stable level. Under some conditions, the fluctuations may increase. That is, each increase in density produces a more severe crisis and a greater decline in the population. If the population becomes small enough on one of these fluctuations, it may not recover. There may be so few individuals left that they are unable to reproduce, and the population may disappear entirely, as shown in Figure 5-4b.

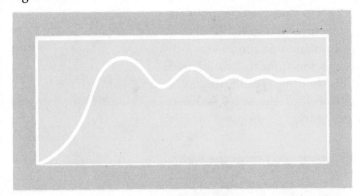

(a) Fluctuations tending to die out

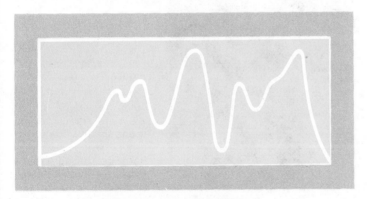

(b) Unstable fluctuations which may lead to disappearance of the population

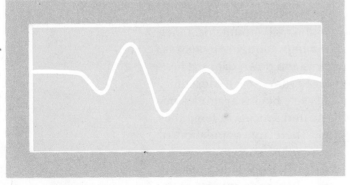

(c) Fluctuations introduced into a stable population (perhaps by a severe winter or drought)

Figure 5–4

Some of the other patterns of growth that occur in populations in nature.

A severe winter, a drought, a sudden influx of predatory animals or human hunters, introduction of a disease, or other such disturbing factors may cause fluctuations to begin in a population that had been at a fairly steady level (Figure 5-4c). We saw one example of such a population curve in Chapter 1. The deer of the Kaibab forest had reached a fairly stable population of about 4000 individuals. When they were protected from their predators, the death rate was greatly lowered. As a result, the population increased rapidly to a peak of about 100,000 deer after 18 years. Then, as we saw earlier, it dropped rapidly, to only 10,000 deer.

Figure 5–5

Lemmings (left) and voles (opposite page) are both small rodents found in the Canadian arctic whose populations go through sharp increases every three or four years.

The most dramatic example of population fluctuation in nature is that of the lemmings in the Scandinavian countries of northern Europe. These little animals, very similar to mice, normally live in the high mountains. Once in a while, the number of lemmings suddenly increases. They swarm out of the mountains and down over the lowlands in great numbers, seeking food. Within a short time, the population crashes and the cycle begins again. A similar cycle is found among the related species of lemmings of the Canadian arctic region. There the population of lemmings and of meadow mice (voles) shows a sharp increase about every 3 or 4 years. The predators feeding upon the voles and lemmings, such as foxes and owls,

"I don't care if I am a lemming—I'm not going."

also increase in numbers as their food source expands. When the populations of lemmings and voles crash, the predator populations follow.

Some measures of this cycle over many years are available because records have been kept of the numbers of fox skins sold by trappers in the region. Although these numbers are affected by other factors, such as the number of hunters and trappers in the area, they give a rough

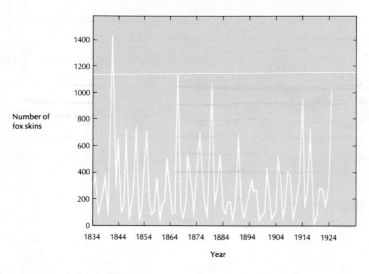

Figure 5–6

Fluctuations in the number of fox skins obtained in a part of Labrador over a 90-year period. Foxes in this area feed on voles, and their population explosions and crashes closely parallel those of the vole.

idea of the fluctuations in the fox population. As you can see in Figure 5-6, the fox population showed a sharp increase about every 4 years. These foxes feed mostly on voles, so it is assumed that the vole population was going through a similar cycle. Presumably the great plagues of lemmings in Scandinavia represent unusually high population peaks in a similar cycle.

It is easy to understand why the population of foxes would increase when vast numbers of voles made it almost impossible for a fox to starve to death. Similarly, crashes in the fox population would be the result of starvation when the vole population suddenly declined. But what causes the cycles in the vole population?

One possible explanation involves interactions between three populations: voles, foxes, and grass. When the voles are abundant, they eat most of the grass and small shrubs in the area during the winter. Without this cover to hide under, they are easy prey for the foxes and hunting birds, which increase greatly in numbers as they feed richly on the helpless voles. The food shortage and great loss to predation causes a crash in the vole population. Within a year or two, the plant cover grows back, and the few remaining voles are able to avoid the now-starving predators. With voles few in number and well hidden, the predators are unable to get enough food, and their populations crash. Once the food is abundant again and the predators few, the population of voles increases rapidly, and the cycle begins again.

Figure 5–7
The Canadian lynx is largely dependent on the snowshoe hare for food. The graph shown is a record of the pelts of both animals received by the Hudson Bay Company over 90 years. The 9-10 year cycles of the two animals are obviously related. An increased hare population provides food for the lynxes, which in turn increase in number. The hare population declines soon after. What happens next to the hare population and why?

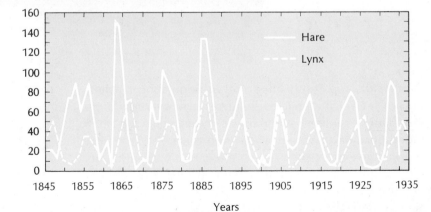

Number in thousands

Years

In North America, many animal populations seem to go through similar cycles, most commonly with peaks about 10 years apart. The snowshoe hare, muskrats, grouse, pheasant, and quail all seem to experience a 10-year population cycle. The predators that feed upon these animals are also affected.

This cycle is much more difficult to understand, because it affects so many different kinds of animals over such a wide area. For example, 1942 was a year of peak population for snowshoe hares both in Canada and as far south as the Appalachian Mountains of West Virginia. Ruffed grouse in the Midwest and pheasants in Iowa were also reported to be unusually numerous that year.

It is difficult to see how a predator–prey relationship could cause this cycle to recur so regularly over such a huge area. In fact, some experiments with grouse in controlled areas have shown that the cycles continue—and may even become more extreme—when predators and human hunters are kept away from the prey animals.

Some have suggested that the 10-year cycle is caused by long-term variations in weather, perhaps related to a regular change in solar radiation. Others have argued that the cycle does not really exist, but is merely a result of random variations in rather imperfect statistics. Most ecologists, however, believe that the cycle is real and that some explanation will be found in terms of the interacting populations of the ecosystem.

The Effects of Overcrowding on Populations

One factor, apparently important in population crashes, but not yet well understood, is the result of overcrowding. Most kinds of animals seem to react in peculiar ways when the population density becomes too great.

In the early 1960's some now-famous experiments were begun with small populations of rats. A few dozen rats were placed in 100-foot square pens in which unlimited food, water, and air were available. The rats were studied for as long as 2 years. At the normal reproduction rate, an eventual population of 5,000 adult rats could have been expected. Yet, the rat population never increased beyond 150 to 200 adults, depending on the experiment. Many young were produced, but few survived to adulthood. Such experiments have been repeated many times since, all with similar results.

The rat pens have no shortage of food, no predators, and no disease epidemics under the conditions of the experiments. What, then, causes the populations to stabilize at such low levels? The controlling factors seemed to be changes in the behavior and social organization of the animals themselves. These changes resulted in high infant death rates, and often in low fertility. Regular courtship and mating behavior was lost. Females apparently forgot how to build nests or care for their young. Neglected young were eaten by many of the adult rats, although rats are not usually cannibals.

Similar results are being obtained today with experiments on mice in crowded cages. Normal behavior breaks down. The mice, like the rats, fail even to make best use of the available space. Again, infant mortality rates are high, and the breeding rate falls off.

These and other experiments suggest that if a large number of animals is placed in a small space, so that overcrowding occurs before normal social patterns can be

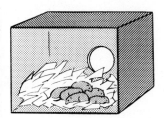
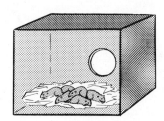

Figure 5–8

A normal mother rat builds a fluffy nest, as shown in the top left-hand drawing. Two weeks later it is flattened by the young, but still gives adequate protection and warmth. The unfinished nest shown in the bottom left-hand drawing was built by a disturbed female raised in a crowded pen. At the right, two weeks later, one of the young has already left and another is about to leave. They cannot survive alone.

established, fights and other unusual behavior begin to occur even though plenty of food, water, and nesting material are available. It appears that overcrowding can cause physical disease, brought on by the stresses of crowding. In the abnormal competition and conflict, the balance of the chemical systems in the body is disturbed. The blood sugar levels drop drastically, and an animal may even enter a fatal state of shock, much like that resulting from a severe injury.

Some biologists have proposed that this shock disease may be the major cause of death in most population crashes. Others have questioned the studies on which this conclusion is based. More experimental work remains to be done. Of course, in the natural environment, when a population is both very large and very crowded, disease organisms and parasites have many opportunities to find hosts and move from host to host.

On the other hand, there seems to be a *minimum* population level for successful reproduction as well. Some birds, for example, simply will not nest if the population density becomes too low. Plant and animal populations may die out if population density becomes so low that an individual of one sex is unlikely to encounter one of the other sex in order to reproduce. Factors such as these may lead to the disappearance of a population if a crash carries the density below a certain minimum level. Bird species, such as the Eskimo curlew, have gone extinct in recent years in this way. This fate may also be in store for several species of the great whales. These range over millions of square miles of the oceans, but have been overhunted by man so badly that whaling expeditions are unable even to catch the limited quotas that have been set for the various kinds of whales.

Claiming a Territory

The spacing of a population over an area often shows the phenomenon called *territoriality*. An individual or small group tends to claim an area as its own, and to drive other animals of the same kind out of the territory. In many cases, successful breeding and rearing of young is only carried out in an established territory. The stronger, more dominant animals claim their territories and reproduce; those driven to the fringes do not produce offspring. This behavior seems to be a very important natural limit upon population growth in most kinds of animals.

In most cases, little combat is involved in establishing and defending territories. An animal in its own territory is confident and sassy. It marks out its domain by clear signals of one sort or another. Birds sing noisily or display their bright feathers from prominent points in their territory. Rabbits mark out territories with small piles of droppings. Dogs, wolves, and coyotes urinate at points along the fringes of their territory. These signals warn other animals that the territory is occupied. An intruder is ill at ease and appears very unsure of himself. If he should venture into the territory, a ceremonial show of force or threat from the tenant is usually enough to send the intruder packing.

Some kinds of animals defend their territories against all intruders of the same kind. Others protect only a small area for nesting, while sharing common feeding areas with others of the same kind. Still others do not appear to claim territories at all. In such cases, each individual may have a home range where he tends to stay, but he makes no attempt to keep out other animals of the same kind.

The study of territorial behavior is still going on, and there is much yet to be learned. It appears now that this type of behavior is much more common in the animal world than anyone suspected a few years ago. It may be one of the most important natural means of keeping populations within an ecosystem relatively stable.

A Population:
Members of the Same Species

The organisms which make up a population are said to be members of the same *species*. We have said that a population consists of the same kind of animals or plants. That is, they are similar in appearance and behavior, and are capable of interbreeding. It is clear that dogs and horses are members of different species. However, all of the many different types of dogs are usually considered to be members of the same species. This is because they can all successfully interbreed, producing offspring that can also interbreed. On the other hand, the red squirrel and the grey squirrel are considered two different species. They will not interbreed if they live in the same area, and will form two separate populations. American caribou and European reindeer appear identical to us, but if they are

Figure 5–9

The American caribou (left) and the European reindeer, although they seem identical, do not produce fertile offspring when they breed. For this reason they are considered separate species.

interbred, the offspring are sterile; the next generation cannot breed.

The exact nature of a species, how it is formed and how it may change, is the subject for another long study. Scientists, in fact, debate just what it is that constitutes a species. Of course the idea of successful breeding gives a strong rule-of-thumb. However, without worrying about the details of the subject, we shall find it useful to use the word.

A population is made up of individuals belonging to a single species. There might be another population of the same species in the next valley or another biome. However, if these two populations were brought together, they would be able to interbreed. Where two *different* species live together, no matter how similar they may appear to us, they will form two different populations which may increase or decline independently. Each species will occupy a different niche in the habitat.

Communities

At this point, it might be useful to return to our original idea of an ecosystem. The ecosystem was said to be composed of a nonliving environment and a community of living organisms. The *community* in turn is made up of populations, each of which is made up of individuals of a single species.

When we were looking at the relationships between grass, voles, and predators, we were in a sense looking at a community. These three organisms always go together. Of course, you know that the community that contained the voles, the grass they ate, and the predators that ate voles was more complicated than that. You can guess that there were other plants, insects that also fed on grass or other plants, animals that ate the insects, decomposers in the soil, and so on. Interactions in this community were not simply between voles, predators, and grass, but between all the populations present, of whatever species.

In Chapter 4 we saw that each population is limited in its occupation of an area by its tolerances for various conditions in the environment—both living and nonliving. The factors that limit the range are slightly different for each species. Thus the various populations in a community occupy slightly different areas. In most cases, it is impossible to draw a firm line around a community. Some organisms spread into adjacent communities. Others migrate back and forth from one community to another.

If we are to understand ecosystems completely, we must consider the entire earth as a single ecosystem. As we saw in the simple case of two populations interacting through predation, some problems can be understood only in the light of a fairly large ecosystem. In any case, we should be cautious about drawing firm conclusions from study of a small area. Although a community may seem relatively isolated, it probably overlaps in important ways with other parts of the earth's ecosystem.

We know so little about the millions of interactions that keep the complex ecosystem of the earth in operation that we can make only the roughest guesses about the effects of large changes made by man. Yet these changes are being made all the time.

Some ecologists have suggested that we think of ourselves as passengers on Spaceship Earth. The ecosystem is the incredibly complex life-support mechanism that supplies our food, air, water, and other needs. We know practically nothing of the detailed workings of this mechanism. Yet we are busily destroying parts of it, and inserting new parts as rapidly as we can. The rate at which mankind is introducing changes has been increasing greatly in our lifetime. It would seem wiser to tamper as little as possible until we know more about what we are doing. Otherwise we may come to regret our hasty and possibly permanent changes in the ecosystem.

Before we can deal with man's changes in the ecosystem, however, we should look at the way communities and ecosystems change naturally through time. The next chapter will be devoted to this.

Test Yourself

1. What is a population? What is the name of a local grouping of different kinds of interacting populations?
2. All individuals of a population are the same kind of organism, and so all belong to the same_____.
3. How are birth and death rates related in the growth or decline of a population?
4. What is the observed effect of overcrowding on animals, even when food, water, and other needs seem to be ample? How does this affect population size?
5. Biologists and other scientists believe, on various kinds of evidence, that the over-all human birth rate has not changed in any real way for 100,000 years or more. Yet, the earth's human population doubled between 1880 and 1970, and is expected to double again by the year 2000. What do you suppose has happened?

6. From what you have read in this chapter, do you suppose the number of owls in a meadow controls the number of mice, or is it perhaps the other way around? Discuss.
7. Population explosions often start with just a few individual organisms entering an ecosystem where there is plenty of food, space, and other necessities, and few predators. Population density is low at first. Yet, if a population "crashes" to rather few individuals it may die out completely. Why should this be? Discuss.
8. Do human beings show any signs of territorial behavior? If so, what?
9. Why were space scientists once so concerned about the possibility that germs from the moon might be brought back to the earth by the first Project Apollo astronauts?
10. The grass, voles, and foxes of the Arctic discussed in this chapter belonged to a community that contained many other organisms that were not listed. But do human beings belong to a community of this kind? If so, what else is in it? Discuss.

Changes Through Time

Changes in an Abandoned Farm

A mature forest does not seem to change very much from year to year. Some animals die. New ones are born. Old plants also are replaced by new individuals. The density of populations may change somewhat. There may be more or fewer foxes or oak trees at one time than at another. Yet a mature forest looks much the same today as it did 50 years ago.

Of course, major crises such as fires or floods may destroy or change an ecosystem. Today the human population is altering almost every ecosystem on earth. Lumbering, road building, construction, hunting, farming, and other human activities have left few ecosystems in their natural state.

What does happen to an ecosystem when it is disturbed? Where fire, flood, or human activities have greatly changed an ecosystem, we can observe changes that occur rather swiftly during the following years. These rapid changes give us some clues about the slow changes that go on in undisturbed ecosystems.

One example that has been carefully studied is that of an abandoned farm or field. In creating the field, man clears off the natural plant cover and drives out or kills most of the animals. He replaces the natural plant cover with his crops. He supplies water, fertilizer, and care such as plowing and weeding to help the crops grow. He uses chemicals to keep insects and other pests away from his crops.

If a farm is abandoned, the ecosystem on the field goes through a sequence of changes which return it to a state much like that before the farmer arrived. We shall look at the well-studied case of such abandoned fields in the oak–hickory forest region of the southeastern United States.

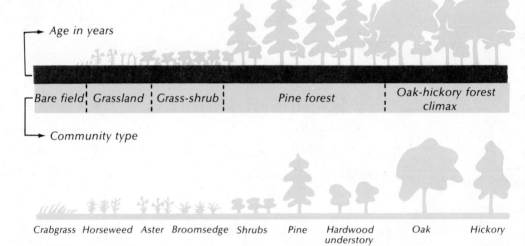

Crabgrass Horseweed Aster Broomsedge Shrubs Pine Hardwood understory Oak Hickory

Figure 6–1

A succession from a bare field to an oak–hickory forest as it occurred over 150 years in the piedmont region of the southeastern United States.

Many years ago, someone cut down the oak and hickory trees, grubbed out the stumps, cleared off the shrubs, and made a farm. Over the years since, other farmers have used the land. They have plowed and hoed and fertilized and watered. Each year they have harvested a crop of cotton or corn from the land. They have sprayed chemicals to keep out unwanted insects, animals, and weeds.

Now the farm has been abandoned. What happens to the land when humans no longer mold it to their purposes? In many studies at different times and places, a remarkably similar sequence has been observed.

Weeds begin to spring up everywhere. Since they are the first species to arrive, they are fittingly called *pioneers*. Most of the cotton or corn plants that remain are soon crowded or shaded out by the weeds. These weeds are plants that grow quickly in open sunlight with limited water. They thrive on soil that has been plowed up or disturbed. They grow swiftly, reaching full size in a few weeks and producing huge numbers of seeds. If there is a dry spell, they die just as swiftly. But they leave behind their seeds, which can survive on or in the ground for months or years. When conditions are right again, the seeds sprout and the carpet of weeds appears again. Most have seeds that are scattered widely by the wind, by running water, or by sticking in the coats of animals.

The crop plants cannot survive under such conditions. They need careful planting, fertilizer, water, and open space without competition from the weeds. They are so specialized that they cannot live without man's help and care.

Most of the weeds, also, are plants that live only where man has disrupted the ecosystem. Many are not natives of the southeastern woods, but have come from Asia, Africa, or Europe as unnoticed and unwanted stowaways. They live in places where man has cleared the ground—on roadsides, railroad embankments, vacant lots, and in abandoned fields like this one.

Within a few months after the farmer stops weeding, the field is covered with crabgrass, a plant that came with the Europeans to the Americas. Mourning doves and sparrows flock in to feed on its abundant seeds. The crabgrass shades the soil and slows the evaporation of moisture. In its moist shadows, plants of horseweed begin to grow.

The horseweed grows slowly. It needs the protection of the crabgrass to get started. However, by the next spring, the horseweed plants have become so thick and tall that the crabgrass begins to lose in the struggle for sunlight and nutrients. A few small wild aster plants can be found here and there among the horseweed and crabgrass. Although the asters are so tiny as to be almost unnoticed, they produce many seeds during this first summer.

In the second spring, the asters come up in great numbers all over the field. In the soil that has been enriched by the remains of crabgrass and horseweed plants, the aster seeds are now able to find ideal growing conditions. In the second summer the asters dominate the field. Only a few small horseweed plants and scattered patches of crabgrass can be found. Grasshopper sparrows and meadowlarks nest in the field, and a few meadow mice may move in to feed on the seeds.

During the next winter, tall clumps of broomsedge, a grass, begin to poke up among the asters. This slow-growing plant needed rich soil and a long period of time to get started, but now it begins to take over. In the third summer the clumps of broomsedge dominate the field, with asters scattered between the clumps. The thick cover of tall grasses, standing about three feet high, completely shades out the crabgrass. Cotton rats move into the field to eat the broomsedge seeds. Deer may visit to browse on the grasses.

Over the following years, as the soil becomes richer in plant remains and other organic matter, and the shade becomes more dense, shrubs begin to poke up here and there among the grass and asters. The shrubs grow very slowly, but they survive from year to year. While the other plants must start over after each dry spell or freeze, the shrubs steadily get larger. Eventually the asters are shaded out, though the clumps of broomsedge hold their own. At first the shrubs grow in thick patches separated by grassland, wherever the shrub seeds were dropped by visiting birds and animals. As they produce seeds from year to year, the shrubby patches slowly become larger and the grassland disappears.

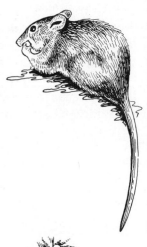

About 15 years after the field was abandoned, the shrubs have taken over much of the area. Sparrows and meadowlarks still nest in scattered grassy spots, but field sparrows and yellowthroats nest in the shrubs over much of the field. Golden mice and white-footed mice live and feed in the shrubs. Foxes and weasels first visit on hunting expeditions, and later move into the field as food becomes more abundant.

By the twentieth year, the grassland and its residents are nearly gone. In the rich soil, shaded by the shrubs and containing the remains of many generations of plants and animals, pine trees begin to push up here and there. It takes a long time for a pine tree to grow, but once its top grows out of the shrub layer for a few feet, it begins to shade out the shrubs beneath it.

By the thirty-fifth year after abandonment, the field has become a pine forest. The trees are small and scattered, with much underbrush and many shrubby clearings. Pine warblers, towhees, and summer tanagers nest in the

Figure 6–2

The weed cover near this abandoned farmhouse was first gradually replaced by shrubs and, after about twenty years, by a cover of young pine trees.

pines. Pine mice, squirrels, skunks, and other forest animals are common. The pine seeds, needles, and bark support a rich variety of insects and other animals. The nature of the soil changes under these influences. The climate on the forest floor becomes cooler, moister, and less windy.

The floor of the pine forest provides ideal growing conditions for oak and hickory trees. At first they form the understory of the forest, gathering the light that filters through the taller pines. In the climate of the southeastern United States, however, they grow more rapidly than the pines. By the hundredth year, they are pushing above the pine trees and beginning to shade them out. Fifty years later, the pine trees are gone and an oak–hickory forest covers the field. It is much like the forest that the long-ago farmer cleared away to create his field. The populations of plants, animals, and birds are similar to those of the undisturbed forests in the region.

The long sequence of communities that occupied the abandoned field has restored the climax vegetation, the oak–hickory forest. This *climax community* seems to be the stable one for this region. Over many further decades of observation, the oak–hickory forest and its community of animals remains essentially unchanged. Of course, there are minor variations from place to place. On shady or sunny hillsides, in moist or dry spots, where the soil is rocky or sandy, slightly different communities exist. Conditions of weather may change from time to time, with resulting rises or declines in certain populations.

Perhaps the oak–hickory forest itself is only another stage in the sequence of communities. In a few centuries it may be replaced by a different community. However, the rate of change has become too slow to be noticeable in a human lifetime. The forest appears to be the climax of this particular sequence of communities.

Hickory

The gradual replacing of one community of plants and animals with another that we have been describing is called a *succession*. In other regions, a different succession may occur. The different conditions of soil, rainfall, temperature, and wind favor the growth of different plants and animals. Each of the temporary communities is different, and a different climax community is reached.

Yet the general pattern of succession is much the same everywhere. Succession occurs in streams, lakes, and ponds. Even bare rock can eventually be turned into productive soil through the process of succession. The hardy organisms called lichens spread their scaly patches over rock faces. The lichens seem to do little to break the rock down into soil, but they provide nooks in which dust and sand can accumulate. There small plants can begin to grow. Their roots slowly break up the rock, and their leaves and branches hold more wind-blown dirt. The debris of the plants and the droppings and bodies of animals and insects that come to feed on them slowly accumulate in the soil layer. After many centuries, the slow succession may turn the bare rock into a productive soil layer that will support the growth of larger plants and trees.

Figure 6–3

How does the plant shown, growing in what seems to be bare rock, contribute to succession in its community?

The Stability of
Climax Communities

We can make a few general observations that apply to most of the examples of succession that have been studied. We have already seen that earlier stages tend to be made up of quickly-growing, short-lived organisms. In these early stages, a new community may replace the old one from one growing season to the next. In later stages, plants tend to survive over many seasons, and changes from one stage to the next are more gradual.

In most cases, the number of different populations in the community and the total biomass of the community seem to increase from each stage to the next. The community becomes more complex as succession goes on. In the abandoned field, the first community consisted almost entirely of crabgrass, two species of birds, and a few species of insects. The climax community of the oak–hickory forest contains hundreds of different species of plants and animals.

Such a complex ecosystem seems to be more stable than a simpler one. A change in weather or the invasion of some kind of insect or virus that attacks plants or animals can seriously damage or even destroy an ecosystem that has only a few species. In a complex community, there are apt to be many more species that survive under the new conditions and grow in numbers to replace the populations that dwindle.

The farmer's field of cotton or corn was a very simple ecosystem. The farmer tried to keep only a single species of plant and perhaps a few useful populations of bees, earthworms, and the like. Constant use of pesticides and weed-killers was needed to keep out the other species that attempted to move into the field.

The open spaces and bare soil of the field provided ideal conditions for the pioneer plants of the natural succession. The farmer spent most of his time trying to keep succession from occurring. Whenever he relaxed his efforts, the crabgrass moved in to begin the sequence that would eventually restore the forest community.

But the farmer paid a price for maintaining his simple ecosystem. It was a very unstable one. A dry spell that hardly affected the surrounding forest might kill off all his crops, which need water in abundance. In the complex forest, insects adapted to particular kinds of plant food seldom become so numerous as to cause major damage. The plants on which they feed are scattered through the forest, and hard to find. Natural predators keep the populations of insects in balance. Population explosions and crashes are rare here.

In the field, however, there is a rich supply of a single kind of food. The use of pesticides or the lack of other kinds of food may have eliminated natural enemies. Thus, if an invasion of some kind of insect gets started, conditions are ideal for a population explosion.

The gardener faces the same problems. When he complains that the weeds seem to grow better than his flowers or vegetables, he is not imagining things. The weeds are the pioneer plants of the local succession. They thrive under the conditions that he has created in his garden—open ground, freshly turned soil, and occasional watering. If he gives them half a chance, they will begin to turn his garden back into the climax community that once existed there.

Lumber producers often face the same situation. They may wish to keep a pine forest in the Southeast, for example. They must constantly intervene to prevent the oak and hickory trees from taking over. If they wish to keep their trees widely spaced and tall for good lumber, but to keep out the undergrowth that blocks their logging operations, they must interfere with the natural process of succession by one method or another.

In many parts of the country, the climax community has changed since European peoples arrived. These changes appear to be due to man's interference with the process of succession, or the maintenance of the climax community. For example, great forests of long-leaf pine covered much of the coastal plain of the southern United States when the Europeans arrived. Today, the oaks and hickories have replaced many of the pines. Since the pines were very valuable as lumber, man has taken a great interest in the reasons for their disappearance.

Surprisingly enough, it now appears that these pines were doomed because people protected the forests from fire! In the earlier climax community, infrequent forest fires were started by lightning or by Indians. The pines were more resistant to fire damage than the hardwoods, and grew more readily in the burned-over soil. The cones of the long-leaf pines, in fact, will not open and release their seeds unless they have been scorched by fire. When man removed fire from the environment, the hardwood populations increased and crowded out the pines. In this case, man's interference permitted succession to proceed to a stage that did not occur in the ecosystem before European man arrived.

Of course, in many kinds of forest, fire is a complete destroyer. A northern white pine forest must be protected from fire. White pines are not adapted to fire as southern long-leaf pines are. What is wise treatment for one kind of forest may not be wise for another.

Man's Changes in the Ecosystem

Today it is almost impossible, particularly in the United States, to find an ecosystem that has not been changed in the past century by man's actions. Even in national parks and wilderness areas, trappers, hunters, lumbermen, campers, and (as we have seen) even fire fighters have altered the balance of the climax communities. In most cases, we have not understood the possible consequences of the changes we made. As ecologists learn more and more about the complexities of the ecosystem, they become ever more alarmed at the possible effects of our changes. In a multitude of examples, the changes have had quite undesirable results. We could fill a very thick book with such stories. Here we will look at just a few examples.

Ragweed is one of the pioneer plants of the natural succession in the Midwest. It grows in abundance on roadsides, vacant lots, abandoned fields, and other areas of bare ground. Unfortunately, many people are allergic to the pollen of ragweed. Abundant ragweed pollen in the air is a major factor in spring outbreaks of hay fever.

If the roadsides and other bare areas were left alone, the ragweed would be crowded out within a year by the plants of the next community: broomsedge, asters, and goldenrods. However, in an attempt to eliminate the source of hay fever, teams of men have been sent out to kill the ragweed with chemicals or fire. This prevents the next community from becoming established, and thus the ground is left bare. The following spring, ragweed appears again in even larger populations.

The results of the ragweed elimination campaign are that ever greater amounts of land are covered by ragweed. Each newly abandoned vacant land grows its own crop. In addition, the old areas have been kept at the ragweed stage of succession by the attacks of fire and chemicals. Seeding of bare ground with plants of later succession stages would be far more effective in cutting down the amount of ragweed pollen.

The cities and industries of man have created a new environment that did not exist a few centuries ago. It is not surprising to find that a climax community of plants and animals has found a home even in the concrete and steel environment of the city. Grasses and other weeds grow in vacant lots and even in tiny dust-filled cracks or ledges in the barest city area. Some birds and many insects make their homes in the cities. In fact, a number of populations are found almost exclusively in human dwellings.

The housefly, the cockroach, the starling, the English sparrow, and the Norway rat are among the species of this community that accompanies man wherever he goes. In addition, there are the wide variety of plants and animals that man intentionally supports as domestic beasts, pets, and crops.

In many areas, lumbering, overgrazing, or pollution from cities or industrial plants has set succession back to an earlier stage. In a few cases, the physical environment has been so severely damaged that the original ecosystem may never be restored. Careless farming or overgrazing may remove the plant cover from a large area and loosen the soil. During a period of drought, the wind may carry

away all of the soil, leaving only bare rock or sterile sand. Huge deserts have been formed in this way.

The new danger that faces the ecosystem today results from the drastic and worldwide nature of the changes being made by modern man. Vast areas are being cleared of plants, paved over, or covered with cities. Many kinds of plants and animals are being destroyed because they seem harmful to man or his crops. Chemical pesticides and weed-killers are sprayed over much of the earth's surface. Rains and runoff carry them into the streams, the lakes, and the oceans.

Even the atmosphere is being altered. Vast amounts of coal and petroleum are burned, pouring smoke and chemicals into the air. Jet planes create ice particles ("vapor trails") in the upper atmosphere. Radioactive materials from atomic test explosions were spread through the air in past decades. These materials give off radiation, which can be harmful to living matter.

Figure 6–4

Strip mining, in this case for coal in West Virginia, cuts giant gashes through the earth, dumping the "overburden" along the way, and destroying all natural systems in its path.

We do not know what effects all of these changes will have. Only recently have we begun to understand the effects of DDT and related chemical insecticides on the environment. DDT, developed during World War II, was first used as an insecticide against the mosquito that carries the dread disease malaria. It was very effective in controlling this disease among Allied troops. Since World War II, it has been used by crop growers to control crop-destroying insect populations and increase the food supply for the growing population. Now we are beginning to see some of the effects of DDT that we did not foresee 25 years ago. Some animal species are dying out because of DDT and its chemical relatives. California pelicans, bald eagles, and ospreys are producing fewer young every year. These birds take in DDT with their food and it causes the females to lay thin-shelled eggs. Experiments have shown that DDT also interferes with photosynthesis by certain green algae in the sea. There is still another effect of DDT that we must consider. Insect species quickly develop immunity to the insecticide. Because of hereditary differences, some insects in a population are resistant to the chemical. They survive its use and produce offspring that are also resistant. Finally, after several generations, a particular strain of insects may be immune to DDT.

Why is DDT so troublesome? For one thing, living organisms concentrate it in their tissues. In a food web, animals take in and may retain the chemicals contained

Figure 6–5

In 1970, only one pelican was observed to hatch in the biggest pelican rookery in California. Concentrated DDT in the mother bird seems to affect the calcium content of the eggshell, so that it is not strong enough to withstand incubation.

in the organism they are eating. For another thing, DDT is a persistent chemical. That is, it does not break down into simpler, harmless substances, at least not very quickly. Many chemicals can be broken down simply by air and sunlight. Others are broken down by the digestive action of bacteria and other organisms. DDT is not. Yet it is biologically active—it enters the body processes of many kinds of organisms. Some of it is changed, but into substances that are still harmful. One of these is DDE, also a poison. And in the reproductive organs of birds and other animals, DDT and DDE disturb hormone balance and the production of calcium compounds for eggshells. There may also be other harmful effects that have not been discovered yet.

DDT is only one example of many persistent chemicals that have harmful effects. There is a class of chemicals used in making plastics, paints, and rubber called PCBs. The PCBs come into the environment as factory wastes and are sometimes released when plastics are burned. The PCB chemicals have harmful effects on bird reproduction. They may also have other as yet unnoticed effects. But 20 years ago, few could foresee the bad effects of DDT. Like DDT, the PCBs are persistent. Most of the DDT ever produced in the world is still in the environment. The PCB materials may be piling up also.

The pesticides, the chemicals in industrial smoke, radioactive materials, and DDT are only a few of many examples of pollution of the environment. Pollution always seems to be harmful in some way. Yet, some scientists point out we do not even know how many kinds of pollution, and how much, we are introducing. Mankind uses hundreds of thousands of different chemicals nowadays, most of which end up in the environment somewhere as waste.

In the past, succession could always reclaim any damaged area, because pioneer species could move in from undisturbed regions nearby. Today man is killing off many of these pioneer species because some are the weeds and pests that attempt to take over his fields. He is changing conditions all over the world without a clear understanding of the effects of his actions on the ecosystem. The possibility now exists that some crucial link in the complex system that supports life on earth will be destroyed all over the planet. If this happens, there will be no undisturbed area from which pioneer species can come to begin the process of succession.

It is this frightening possibility that causes ecologists to urge a slowdown in our changes of the earth. We need more information about the effects of our actions, they say. We must understand the possible results before we spread new materials over the earth, through the oceans, or in the atmosphere. By the time we see the first signs of damage, it may be too late to save the ecosystem.

One scientist stated the problem bluntly: "We are approaching an environmental crisis of unprecedented magnitude, perhaps the first time in the earth's history when one species has threatened the survival of the biosphere." Unless we are very lucky, the survival of man—indeed, of all life on earth—will depend upon a better understanding of our environment and our determination to protect the ecosystem. Some young ecologists have suggested the slogan: "Earth: love it or leave it."

Test Yourself

1. What is meant by succession in an ecosystem?
2. What are pioneer organisms in an ecosystem or community? Are they merely first arrivals? What do they do?
3. In what specific ways do southern long-leaf pine forests depend on fire for their maintenance? What happens if fire is always prevented?
4. Why, in general, is a complex ecosystem more stable than a simpler one?
5. From this chapter, give two clear-cut examples of self-defeating attempts by man to improve or reshape his ecosystem to some particular human end.
6. Many things that mankind does are not intended to produce any changes in the ecosystem. But what is the risk to many of the things we do, such as introducing ever-growing numbers of new chemicals in our industrial processes?

7. As you have seen, farmers have problems setting up simplified ecosystems for the growing of a crop. Could a farmer set up a more complex ecosystem in some way? Would it have disadvantages?

8. Some ecologists argue that it is very important to preserve every kind of plant and animal on earth, and to protect all species threatened with extinction. They say that this is not just a desire to keep a few samples for our enjoyment or education, but that it may be vital to the survival of the ecosystem. Why?

9. Can the community of human beings—made up of many different national populations—be considered in the light of ecological ideas? Is there a succession of human communities that occupies a new area of exploration and settlement? What is the human climax community?

7

Freshwater Ecosystems

The Importance of
Water Ecosystems

Because man lives on land, we find it easiest to study and think about the forest, the desert, and other land biomes. We tend to forget that water covers three quarters of the surface of our planet. The living things of the oceans, lakes, and streams have not seemed very important to man. Of course, fish, crabs, lobsters, and other large water creatures have been important sources of food over the centuries, but they could always be caught as needed.

It is only within the past century that man has really begun to understand the underwater ecosystems of the earth. In the past decades, the development of diving equipment and instruments for making photographs and measurements in deep water have made more precise observation possible. The danger of a food shortage on land has caused people to begin thinking about farming the sea.

It has become clear that water ecosystems play a very important role in the total ecosphere. Many of our natural resources come from rocks that once formed as sediments underwater. Much of our garbage and waste is swept away by streams into lakes and the oceans. Even the nature of our atmosphere depends greatly upon the heat and gases exchanged over the vast ocean surface.

If we are to understand our environment, we must understand these submerged ecosystems. Furthermore, because of the concentration of pollutants in streams and lakes, it is here that we can see most clearly some of the results of modern man's changes in the environment.

Since the water surface forms a sharp boundary with the land, a small pond (or even an aquarium) may be a good example of a nearly closed ecosystem. You can probably find such an ecosystem near your home or classroom. If so, study it to check and supplement the information in this chapter. Many important discoveries in ecology have come from persons who had the patience to carefully watch the life in such a small ecosystem over months or years, and to think about what they saw.

An Unusual Property
of Water

Many kinds of plants and animals live in small bodies of fresh water. The world beneath the water surface may support a very complex community. Before we look at what is living there, we need to know a little about the physical environment of the pond or lake. (For all practical purposes, a pond is simply a small lake. From now on, we'll use the word *lake* to refer to a body of fresh water that is not flowing very rapidly, regardless of its size. Unless otherwise indicated, most of the ideas given here can be applied to anything from a huge lake to a tiny puddle.)

As you might guess, one important factor in the physical environment of a lake is temperature. But temperature is important for a reason you might not have thought of. When it comes to temperature, water is a very unusual substance.

Most substances contract (shrink) as they get colder. Most liquids go on contracting as they are cooled until they solidify, or freeze. The frozen liquid, now a solid, continues to contract when cooled further. As a substance contracts, its *density* increases. That is, any given volume of it (such as a cubic inch or cubic foot) weighs more than the same volume of the same substance at a higher temperature. We usually say that the colder a substance gets, the heavier it gets. What we mean is that it has more mass (or weight) per unit of volume—it is more dense.

You may already know that water does not behave like an ordinary liquid as it is cooled. It becomes more dense, as expected, until it reaches a temperature of about 4°C. At this temperature, water reaches its maximum density. If cooled further, water becomes *less dense*! And when it freezes, at 0°C, it expands considerably. For this reason, ice floats in water. In almost every other substance, the solid form is more dense and sinks in the liquid form. Why is this important? Because it means that most lakes and rivers never freeze to the bottom. This has important consequences for living organisms, even for land dwellers. Let's see how this works.

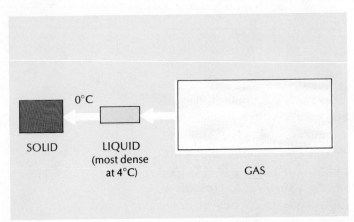

Figure 7–1
Ice is less dense than liquid water. That is, the same mass of water occupies more space as a solid than as a liquid. How does this property affect the lake ecosystem in winter?

In the winter, a lake may freeze over at the surface. Below the ice, however, the water will be slightly warmer. Near the bottom of the lake, the densest water, of a temperature of about 4°C, will collect. The layer of ice at the surface helps to insulate this water, slowing down the rate at which it cools. Unless the water is very shallow, ice is unlikely to form all the way to the bottom, even in a very long and cold winter. Fish and other animals are able to live through the winter beneath the ice.

If ice were more dense than water, it would sink to the bottom. The warmer water would rise to the surface, lose heat energy, and be frozen in turn. Most lakes would freeze solid from bottom to top during the winter, and plants and animals would be killed. In fact, even during the summer much of the ice in the deep lakes would be protected from the sun's warmth and would not melt. Our climate would be much cooler. Not many freshwater plants and animals would be able to live far from the equator. The fortunate peculiarity of water—that it is less dense as a solid than as a liquid—has very important results for life on earth!

As the spring brings longer hours of brighter sunshine, the heat energy melts the ice on the surface of a lake. The surface layer of water begins to become warmer. Its density increases. When the temperature of the surface layer reaches 4°C, the water of this layer begins to sink. Then the less dense water beneath it moves up to the top. As this new top layer is warmed to 4°C, it too sinks and is replaced by cooler, less dense water. This mixing process is called the *spring overturn* of the lake.

During the overturn, oxygen-rich water from the surface is mixed through the lake. The deep water, whose oxygen was largely used up by plants and animals beneath the ice during the winter, is brought to the surface, where it can absorb more oxygen. Minerals and organic remains that have settled to the bottom are circulated through the lake.

As summer approaches and the sun's heat becomes more intense, the upper layer becomes still warmer. When its temperature becomes higher than 4°C, it is again less dense than the bottom layers. Thus the top layer no longer has a tendency to sink, and the mixing process stops.

Through the summer, the deep water—protected from heat by the surface layer—remains cool. Animals, plants, and decomposer bacteria again use up much of the oxygen dissolved in the deep water. Organic remains and minerals again collect in the deeper waters.

As autumn arrives, days become shorter and colder. Heat is removed from the surface layer and its temperature drops. When the surface layer cools to a temperature of 4°C, the fall overturn takes place. Again the waters of the whole lake are stirred and mixed, aided by the wind. As the temperature continues to fall, the surface layer again becomes less dense and eventually begins to freeze. The yearly cycle begins again.

Sunlight and Food
in the Lake Ecosystem

Just as in the forest ecosystem, the basic source of food energy for the lake ecosystem is sunlight. Plants use the sunlight to turn carbon dioxide and water into a usable form through photosynthesis. Primary consumers eat the plants. Secondary and tertiary consumers eat the plant-eaters. Decomposers feed on the remains of organisms that die, breaking down their bodies into simple materials that can be re-used by the plants.

But, unlike the land ecosystems, the lake ecosystem

has a very limited area where sunlight is available. Water absorbs sunlight, turning it into heat energy. Red light is absorbed very rapidly. At a depth of only 1 meter, most of the red light in sunlight has been absorbed by the water. Blue light travels farther through the water, so that everything begins to take on a blue-green tinge to a human observer under water. If mud, silt, or other tiny particles are suspended in the water, the light is absorbed very rapidly.

Clearly, the plants—the primary producers—of the lake ecosystem must live near the surface of the water, where they are able to capture sunlight. In shallow water, where sunlight reaches the bottom, rooted plants such as water lilies, sedges, and rushes can grow.

Out in deeper water, the plants must float at or near the surface. Few large plants have adapted to this floating life. Most of the plants in the lake are microscopic, and these account for most of the photosynthesis that occurs in the lake. As you might expect, the microscopic plants are fed upon first by microscopic animals. The food web builds up from there to fish and other large organisms. The microscopic life forms simply drift in the waters of the lake. They are not true swimmers. The general name for this collection of drifting life is *plankton*. The term comes from a Greek root meaning "wanderer". It covers many species of plant and animal. For convenience, the plankton plants are often termed *phytoplankton* (the Greek *phyto* = plant). The animals are termed *zooplankton* (*zoi* = animal). The phytoplankton are mostly made up of species of algae, often single-celled, including special types called *diatoms*. Most people are not even aware of their existence, but these form the bottom links of most of the food chains in the lake. Most phytoplankton are unable to swim in any way, but they have various adaptations that keep them drifting in the sunlit upper layers (see Figure 7-2). They must have sunlight, of course, for photosynthesis.

The zooplankton, on the other hand, are able to swim, though not strongly. Some species move to different levels in the lake in winter or summer. Many species move up or down from day to night. They may stay in the deep water at night, moving up to feed on the phytoplankton in the daytime. Other animals show just the opposite movements.

After the spring overturn, when the upper layer is rich in nutrients stirred up from the bottom, a great population increase of phytoplankton often occurs. This is called the *spring bloom*, and it may even cause the water to appear greenish. Later in the summer, as the nutrients are used up, the population of phytoplankton normally declines.

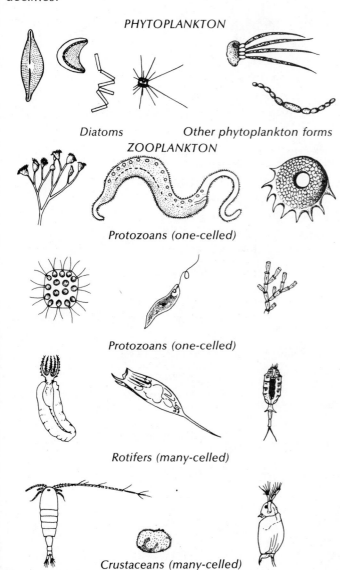

PHYTOPLANKTON

Diatoms   Other phytoplankton forms

ZOOPLANKTON

Protozoans (one-celled)

Protozoans (one-celled)

Rotifers (many-celled)

Crustaceans (many-celled)

Figure 7–2

Phytoplankton — microscopic green plants — are the lake's producers. They are able to use the energy of sunlight to manufacture food. Numerous forms of zooplankton, both one-celled and multicellular, are the primary consumers.

Larger organisms, such as fish, are able to swim freely through all levels of the lake. Some spend the winter in deeper waters, moving to the surface layers in the summer. Others feed just under the ice, where a limited population of phytoplankton survives on the dim sunlight, during the winter, and move downward to feed on the debris drifting from above during the summer.

In the deeper water of the lake, temperatures are low, and light is dim or nonexistent throughout the year. Plants cannot live here. The debris drifting down from the surface layers—mostly dead plants and animals—becomes the food for the deep-water dwellers. The decomposers live here, using up oxygen as they break down the remains of the other organisms. In addition, a few fish are able to live in the deep waters. These are species adapted to the cold, the darkness, and the scarcity of oxygen. But only during the overturns in spring and fall are the deep waters richly populated.

In the bottom mud itself, many creatures can live if oxygen is available. Worms, crayfish, clams, and insects burrow in the mud, feeding on debris from above, or on each other. Bacteria and other decomposers also dwell in the mud. Where oxygen is scarce or absent in the bottom waters, the mud is almost lacking in life, except for certain kinds of bacteria that need no oxygen to live.

In the zone near shore, where sunlight reaches the bottom, is a rich community. Waterlilies or other plants rooted in the bottom may spread their leaves over the surface. Insects live on and under the floating leaves or among the submerged stems. In slightly deeper water, rooted plants may grow beneath the water surface. Many insects, worms, and snails live in these submerged "grasslands." Fish and other larger animals feed on these animals.

Succession in a Lake

Streams or rivers carry sediments—mud, silt, and sand—into a lake. Along with the remains of organisms that died in the lake, this material settles to the bottom, slowly filling up the lake basin. As the lake becomes more shallow,

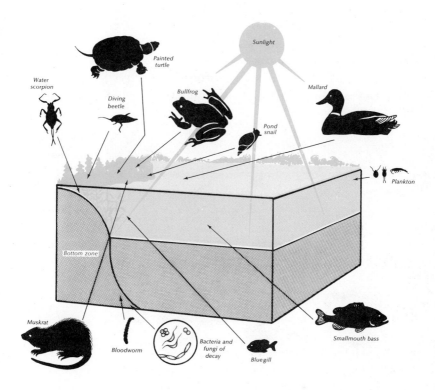

areas near the shore are filled with sediment and pioneer plants of the land ecosystems begin to turn them into grasslands or forests.

While this is going on, changes slowly occur in the water and in the ecosystem. There are even successions of plant and animal life, as there are on land. Also, since lakes receive runoff from the land, the chemicals dissolved in the water change and build up over time. Gradually, lakes tend to become overfertilized by minerals and organic materials from the land. This process is called *eutrophication*, from Greek roots that mean "well nourished." As a result, there is explosive multiplication, or blooms, of certain algae. This leads to the shading out of plants in the deeper waters, and oxygen loss. The lake is well nourished, but dying.

Eventually the shallow lake becomes a marsh or swamp. The process continues until the entire lake basin has been filled with sediment and raised above water

Figure 7–3

A lake may be divided roughly into a near-shore zone, a zone in the open waters into which light penetrates, a deep-water zone, and the zone of the bottom mud. Each zone supports characteristic organisms. The lake in the drawing is shown in midsummer.

level. Then it may remain for a while as a meadow, but eventually is covered by the forest or other climax community of the region. Thus, lakes and ponds are temporary features of the earth's surface.

Swamps and marshes are even shorter lived, though they support a rich and complex community of life while they exist.

Figure 7–4
Lakes undergo succession just as land communities do. The swampy meadow shown was formed from an old lake and, if left alone, will eventually give way to a pine forest.

Running Water

In streams or rivers, the movement of water makes conditions quite different from those in lakes. Except in the deepest or muddiest rivers, sunlight is available throughout the water. At any one point in the stream, the temperature is much the same from bottom to top.

However, conditions do change a great deal from the cold, swift-flowing, clear waters of a mountain stream to the warmer, slowly moving, muddy waters of a large river near the sea. Thus the community varies along the length of a stream rather than from its surface to the bottom.

In the swift mountain streams, oxygen and sunlight are abundant. However, organisms must be able to resist the tearing force of the current. Plants are most abundant in the riffles and rapids, where the stream churns over rocks or pebbles in its channel. Algae and mosses cover the rocks, forming a slippery surface well known to fishermen. Other forms of smaller algae attach themselves to these plants. Many of the plants are carried away by the stream and the scouring action of the sediments that it carries. However, the growth of these plants is very rapid, and losses are soon replaced.

Under the rocks and in the cracks among the rocks and gravel live a variety of animals. Many are the immature forms of insects that spend their later lives in the air. The larvae of mayflies, stoneflies, caddisflies, and alderflies are among them.

These insects apparently depend upon the swiftly flowing and churning water to bring them abundant oxygen. Their breathing structures are not very efficient. They will suffocate in still water. They feed upon the plants and upon organic debris washed down in the current.

Black fly larva and pupa

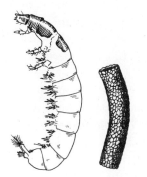

Caddisfly larva and pupa

Mayfly nymph

Stonefly nymph

Figure 7–5

The immature forms of certain insects have various adaptations for life in moving waters. The larva of the black fly, for example, has a sucker that attaches it to a rock, and the black-fly pupa has a "head net" used for straining food from the water. The tubelike caddis-fly pupa faces upstream. Mayfly and stonefly nymphs have streamlined, flattened bodies that enable them to cling to the bottoms of rocks.

In the deeper, stiller water of pools, organic debris and sediments tend to settle. It is here that most of the decomposer organisms of the stream ecosystem live. Water striders, dragonflies, and other organisms not well adapted to swift currents make their homes at the surface. Some fish, such as stream trout, make their homes in the pools, but move into the riffles to feed.

Although most of the stream organisms are able to attach themselves to the rocks, to burrow in the gravel, or to swim powerfully against the current, there is still a steady drift of organisms down the stream. Populations near the head of the stream have a large loss of individuals due to this drift, and must have a high birth rate to keep the population steady.

Farther downstream, the water moves more slowly. Sediments and organic debris settle to the bottom. Temperatures become warmer. The community becomes more similar to that of lakes. Even some plankton are able to survive in the slowly moving waters. The powerful trout are replaced by fish such as bass that are adapted to twisting among the thick plants rather than to fighting current. Many burrowing animals live in the silt on the bottom. The rich supply of organic material drifting downstream supports a large community of decomposers and scavengers. Rooted plants and the animals typical of the nearshore zone of lakes are common.

Pollution of Freshwater Ecosystems

Through the ages, man has often dumped his sewage and garbage into streams or lakes. The running water carried away the unwanted, smelly stuff. In a large lake, it disappeared into the depths without a trace. There was little reason to think about what happened to it.

If a town dumped its sewage into a stream, the water might be discolored and smelly for a few miles downstream. However, within a surprisingly short distance the water again appeared pure and clear.

Some of the sewage was simply spread out through

a large volume of water so that it was less noticeable. Much of it settled to the bottom of pools or lakes where it was buried in the sediments. However, a great deal of it was broken down by the decomposer organisms of the lakes and streams. The decomposers turned it back into simple compounds that could be used by the primary producers of the water ecosystems.

However, as cities became larger and were built closer together, the amount of sewage became so large that it did not disappear. Industrial plants began to pour large amounts of various chemicals into the rivers and lakes. In recent times, detergents that could not be broken down by the decomposers formed layers of suds over the water surfaces.

Figure 7–6
Detergents that cannot be broken down by decomposers (nonbio-degradable detergents) cause blankets of foam such as this one shown in a Florida stream.

Large amounts of water were drawn from the rivers and lakes to cool various industrial plants. The warm water was poured back, greatly changing the natural temperature of the water. Some organisms are very temperature sensitive; some die and others thrive if the temperature changes a few degrees. In this way, local water ecosystems can be changed.

In a swiftly flowing stream, large amounts of sewage can be handled by the ecosystem. The solid matter settles to the bottom, where it is decomposed by bacteria and other organisms. This process uses up oxygen from the water. However, more oxygen is rapidly absorbed at the churning surface of the stream. But chemicals such as carbon dioxide and hydrogen sulfide are released by the decomposers. They may make life impossible in parts of the stream for most fish. As the chemicals are more and more diluted further downstream, the conditions become more normal, and more of the community is able to survive.

However, if the sewage contains poisonous chemicals that are not broken down by the decomposers, much of the life in the stream may be destroyed. These chemicals may be carried for many miles in high enough concentrations to kill most organisms in the stream.

If another town or industrial plant pours its sewage into the stream a short distance downstream, the load of pollutants may become so great that the entire stream community is destroyed. Only the foul-smelling bacteria that live without oxygen remain. The stream becomes a disgusting sewer.

In lakes, particularly large, deep ones, much of the sewage may settle to the bottom. There it is buried in the sediments or decomposed. Here too, large amounts of sewage may cause such an overpopulation of decomposers that the oxygen is used up. All animals die, and only a few bacteria remain.

However, few people will be aware that the hidden deep water of the lake has become a sterile and smelly wasteland. It is only at the spring and fall overturns that the polluted water of the deep layer is brought to the surface where everyone can see and smell it.

Yet, as the temperature continues to change, the layering of water is reestablished, and the problem is once again hidden in the deep layer. People see that the lake appears fresh again, and assume that the problem is solved.

The situation has gotten so bad in some lakes that it cannot be ignored. The Great Lakes of the northern United States are among the most important freshwater bodies of the world. The five lakes contain about 20 percent of all the fresh water on earth. Many of our greatest cities and most important industries depend upon the lakes as a source of water and transportation and as a dumping place for sewage and garbage.

Pollution has become most obvious in Lake Erie, the shallowest of the five lakes. Here the death of the lake ecosystem is not so well hidden in the deep waters. Within the past decade the destruction of life in the lake has become obvious to everyone.

Figure 7–7
The beer can in the midst of the fish dead from industrial pollution is an ironic reminder of man's double disregard for his surroundings.

Man's interference with the natural balance of this lake has reached colossal proportions. Some 5 billion gallons of water are drawn from the lake each day for industrial use. Nearly a billion gallons more are drawn into the water systems of cities around the lake. Similar quantities of sewage and garbage are dumped into the lake, much of it untreated. Further pollution flows into the lake from streams and from the other Great Lakes.

In the 1960's, Lake Erie's problems became too obvious to ignore. The fishermen were first to complain. In 1956, nearly 7 million pounds of blue pike were caught in the lake. By 1963, the total catch of blue pike was only 200 pounds.

However, the average citizen living near the lake had more to complain about than a shortage of fish. Detergent suds coated the water along the shore. Smelly algae covered huge areas of the lake, accumulated on the beaches, and gummed up the water intake pipes. The water contained so much sewage, and such a high concentration of dangerous bacteria, that swimming was forbidden on many beaches. City water systems were able to kill the bacteria in the water, but people still found discolored and smelly water coming from their kitchen taps.

Scientists studying the lake found that—over more than a quarter of the lake—the oxygen concentration in the water had become too low to support life. In the bottom ooze lived mainly the bacteria that need no oxygen and a few pollution-tolerant animals such as sludgeworms, bloodworms, and fingernail clams. The combination of poisonous chemicals, low oxygen, and a lack of food had made life impossible for most fish.

Strangely enough, studies showed that the worst of Lake Erie's problems were due not to poisonous pollutants, but to fertilizers. It was a high level of phosphates and nitrates in the water that caused huge population explosions of algae. With an abundance of these nutrients, the algae grew in thick blankets over the water, choking off sunlight and oxygen for the rest of the ecosystem beneath. As the algae died and sank to the bottom, the populations of decomposers increased enormously, using up more of the oxygen in the water.

Obviously, in Lake Erie the process of eutrophication, mentioned earlier, had been speeded up enormously by the activities of man. Normally, in lakes of this size, eutrophication probably would take hundreds of thousands of years.

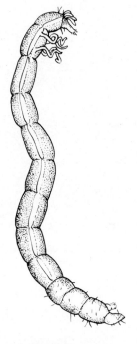

Bloodworm

The phosphates come partially from farmland runoff and from normal sewage. However, the greatest source seems to be from detergents in city and industrial sewage. Laundry detergents contain as much as 70 percent phosphates. During the 1960's, detergent producers learned to produce materials that can be broken down by decomposers (so-called biodegradable detergents). The blankets of suds disappeared. But there is no way to destroy the phosphates, even if the suds no longer appear. Phosphate-free laundry detergents were not available until late in 1970, and are not as popular as the phosphate-rich name brands. Furthermore, cleaning chemicals introduced to replace the phosphate-rich materials have sometimes proved to have their own ecological disadvantages.

The cities and states around the Great Lakes have begun to attack the problem. Cities are attempting to remove more polluting materials from their sewage before dumping it into the lakes. Industries are taking similar steps. However, progress is very slow. Hundreds of millions of dollars would be needed to build adequate sewage plants for the cities, and even greater expenditures would be needed to treat industrial wastes properly.

Around Lake Erie, where the problem is continually obvious to all, some progress is being made. Even so, most scientists believe that it will take centuries for the lake to return to its original state, even if all pollution inflow is halted. Some think that the lake has passed beyond recovery.

On the other Great Lakes, where the worst of the problem is still hidden in deep water, action to stop pollution is even slower. The southern end of Lake Michigan is beginning to approach the condition of Lake Erie. Scientists expect Lake Ontario to follow a similar course very soon.

Even with the best efforts, it seems unlikely that the Great Lakes will again be beautiful and fruitful sites for fishing, swimming, and boating within our lifetimes. Nearly every stream and lake in our country not hidden deep in unsettled territory is more or less polluted.

What happens as phosphates and other pollutants are washed down rivers into the oceans? As we shall see in the next chapter, the ecosystem of the ocean—though less well understood—appears to be far more important to our survival. And it too may be threatened by our pollution.

Test Yourself

1. What is density? How does the density of most substances change with temperature?
2. In what way is water an unusual substance when it comes to temperature?
3. In what way is water's unusual behavior with temperature important to life in the water? And on land?
4. What is meant by spring overturn and fall overturn of a lake? Why do they occur? What benefit do water organisms receive from overturns?
5. What does the name plankton mean, what are the two major kinds, and why do they have this name?
6. Most food chains in a lake begin with what? And end with what? How does this compare with land food chains?
7. What eventually becomes of a lake or pond, given enough time? What is the name of the process of overfertilization and what does it mean?
8. In what ways do various kinds of pollution hasten the aging and death of a lake?
9. Why aren't the effects of pollution of a lake always noticeable?
10. Suppose a lake is shallow enough to allow sunlight to reach all parts of its bottom. How would the ecosystem of such a lake differ from that described in this chapter?
11. Find a book that has pictures and descriptions of plants and animals that live in swiftly-flowing streams. What adaptations enable them to avoid being washed downstream by the rapid currents?
12. The production of living material is greatest in shallow, warm-water lakes. Discuss the reasons for this observation.

13. Find out something about the ecosystems of bogs, marshes, and swamps. How do they differ from those in lakes and streams?
14. Where does your water supply come from? Where do your sewage and garbage go? Are there any present or potential problems of water supply or pollution in your area?

Ocean Ecosystems

The Physical World of the Oceans

It is easy for us to fail to notice the seas as a home for life. We see the oceans as barriers to be crossed in travel, as a surface on which to sail boats, or as providing a nice location for pleasure along the shore. If we think of life in the sea at all, we are apt to think about shells we find on the beach, a few large fish that are caught for food, and perhaps the whales and dolphins.

But these creatures are only a tiny portion of life in the oceans. Seventy percent of the earth's surface is covered by seawater, and living things are found everywhere, from the surface to the deepest trenches in the ocean bottom. On land, most organisms live in the thin layer where ground meets air. But in the sea, the layer containining living things averages between 2 and 3 miles in thickness.

On land, mountain ranges and bodies of water form barriers that keep animals and plants from moving easily. Sea life appears to face no such barriers; all of the seas are connected. However, in the sea, movement can be limited by the temperature and saltiness of the water. As on land, each organism can tolerate certain conditions, and does not survive where conditions are not right for it. Of course there are underwater mountain ranges and other features that can limit the movement of deep-dwelling organisms.

The salt in seawater makes life conditions much different from those in fresh water. The ocean water contains about 3.5 percent of dissolved solids by weight. About 2.7 percent is sodium chloride, ordinary table salt. The remaining 0.8 percent consists of other salts such as calcium carbonate and magnesium sulfate. These dissolved salts play an important part in the ocean ecosystem. They also change the physical properties of the water.

For example, seawater, unlike fresh water, continues to become more dense as it cools, until the freezing point is reached. You will recall that fresh water is most dense at about 4°C. For this reason, water of that temperature tends to collect in the lower layers of lakes. In the ocean basins, bottom water is near 0°C in most places.

Seawater does not freeze at 0°C. The exact freezing point depends on the amount of salt present. The more salt there is, the lower is the freezing point. Some bottom water is as cold as −2°C, well below the freezing point of fresh water. About half the water in the oceans is colder than 2°C, and almost all of it is colder than 7°C. Only in a rather thin surface layer, and in shallow bays and lagoons, are warmer temperatures common.

The salt also affects the density of seawater. The more salt in any given sample, the more dense it is at a given temperature. Oceanographers keep close track of both *salinity* (salt content) and temperature. This helps them identify water types and trace ocean currents.

Currents and Tides

In the tropics, evaporation from the ocean surface is very rapid. Tropical surface water tends to be more saline (salty) than the average for the oceans. However, tropical surface water is also much warmer than average, so it remains less dense. Thus it floats on top of less saline but colder water beneath. As winds push any of this surface water to cooler regions, however, it will cool, gain density, and begin to sink. Somewhere, less dense water will have to rise to replace it. This means that there is a constant slow overturn and other movement of the waters of the ocean. (Lakes, you will recall, turn over only twice a year, in spring and fall.)

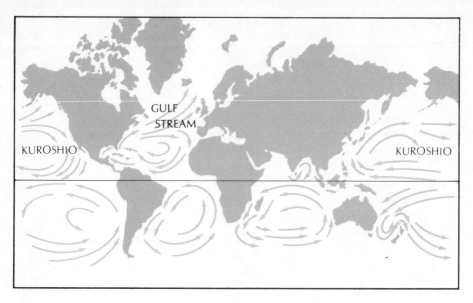

Figure 8–1

The major ocean currents of the world. Note that the Kuroshio eventually becomes a southerly current along the Pacific Coast of the United States, and the Gulf Stream turns south along the west coast of Europe.

Great permanent currents move the waters of the seas. Famous examples of currents are the Gulf Stream in the Atlantic Ocean and the Kuroshio, or Japan current, in the Pacific. Both these warm currents run northward along the western sides of their oceans and eventually turn eastward. With the help of prevailing winds, they carry heat and moisture to the west coasts of the continents on the eastern sides of these oceans—to Europe and to North America. They affect weather and climate very strongly.

Surface currents are generated and driven by the winds. Both wind and water currents are affected by the rotation of the earth, which causes all of them to take curved paths. The major currents rotate around the ocean basins, clockwise in the northern hemisphere and counterclockwise in the southern. Many other currents flow at different levels in the oceans, keeping all the waters in circulation.

Along some shorelines, winds push the surface waters away from the shore. Here, water wells up from the depths to replace surface water. It is this *upwelling* of water from the deeps that explains the unusually high populations of large fish near the western coasts of the

Americas. The upwelling currents bring nutrients which have settled in the deeper layers. This provides fertilizer materials for the marine plants in the sunlit upper layers. The plants, of course, are the start of a food web.

There is another movement of sea waters, more familiar to most people than currents or upwelling. This is the tide that rises and falls twice a day on most shores. The tide results from the gravitational pull of the moon and the sun (but mostly the moon, because it is nearer) on the ocean waters and the earth itself. In the open sea, tidal movement is so slight that it is not even noticeable. Ocean islands may experience a total tidal swing of only a foot or so. But in bays, estuaries (river mouths), and shallow waters near shore, the tidal movement builds up. In some places, the surface of the sea may move up and down as much as 50 feet with the tides. These regular changes of depth are an important part of the physical environment of the shallow-water organisms.

Life Zones in the Sea: The Oceanic Zone

It is convenient to divide up the ocean biome into several smaller units for discussion. Each of these smaller zones has its own typical community of organisms.

At the very edge of the sea there is a specialized zone, where land is exposed to the air during low tide, but covered by water at high tide. This zone is called the *intertidal* zone.

Along most coastlines, the depth of the sea increases very gradually for some miles offshore. As you move away from the coast, the depth of the water gradually increases to about 200 yards. Beyond that depth, the bottom drops off much more steeply. The coastal margin is called the *continental shelf*. The water over it is the *near-shore* zone.

The deeper water beyond the edge of the continental shelf is called the *oceanic* zone. In this zone nearly all of the visible light from the sun is absorbed within a depth of about 200 yards. The deeper waters of the oceanic zone are in perpetual darkness. Since photosynthesis can occur

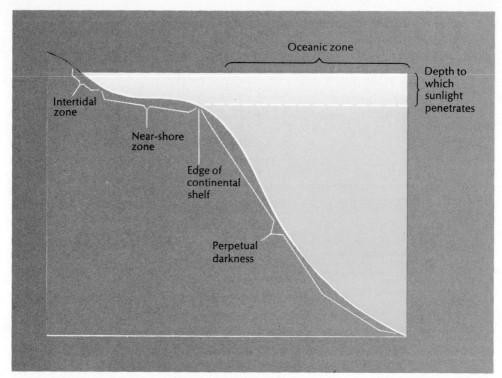

Oceanic zone

Intertidal
zone

Near-shore
zone

Edge of
continental
shelf

Perpetual
darkness

Depth to
which
sunlight
penetrates

only where sunlight is available, none of the producers of the ocean ecosystem live beneath this depth.

The producers of the oceanic zone are almost entirely microscopic floating plants, the phytoplankton. The diatoms are the most common of these tiny one-celled plants, just as they are in lakes. The diatoms probably account for more photosynthesis than any other kind of plant on earth. When the seawater looks green or brownish-green to you, it is probably full of diatoms. There are many kinds, all beautiful to look at under the microscope. Each cell is surrounded by a tiny two-part case of silica, a form of glass. Often many of these single cells are linked together like the jewels in necklaces and bracelets (Figure 8-3).

Figure 8–2

Oceans, like lakes, may be divided into broad zones which have characteristic forms of life.

Figure 8–3

The principal producers of the ocean are these tiny diatoms that resemble precious jewels when viewed under the microscope.

The dinoflagellates are another prominent form of phytoplankton found in the oceanic zone. The dino-flagellates are single-celled forms that carry on photo-synthesis like plants, but have tiny whiplike tails (flagella) which enable them to swim about like animals (see Figure 8-4). High population densities of some kinds of dinoflagellates produce the "red tides" sometimes seen along sea shores. Other kinds give off light, making the seawater glow during the night.

Though they are almost unseen by man (in fact, they were not noticed by scientists until 1845), these two kinds of microscopic plants must serve as the basis of nearly all food chains in the oceanic zone. Because the oceans cover so much of the earth's surface, the phytoplankton probably produce more oxygen and capture more of the sun's energy than all of the other plants on earth combined.

It may surprise you to learn that seaweeds play hardly any part in the ecology of the open sea. Seaweeds are large, multicelled forms of algae that need to be attached to the bottom. Seaweeds are organisms of the shoreline and are missing from most of the oceanic zone.

Land plants and rooted plants in shallow waters can draw minerals and other nutrients from the soil. The plants of the oceanic zone must depend entirely upon the materials dissolved in the water. Phytoplankton seem to be most abundant where surface waters are high in phosphate content. Their distribution in the ocean is patchy, and varies from season to season. Local abundance of other nutrients (such as nitrates) may serve to limit their range. The temperature and salinity of the water also affect the distribution of species.

During the winter, phytoplankton populations dwindle. Days are short; there is not much sunlight for photosynthesis. Surface water temperatures are low. However, nutrients are being released to the water by decomposer bacteria. With the first temperature rise of spring, there is usually a sudden bloom of phytoplankton. Days are longer, and there is more sunlight for photo-synthesis. This blooming may continue into the early summer if nutrients are plentiful. Where upwelling brings nutrient-rich deep water to the surface, the blooms are especially dense and long-lasting.

Figure 8–4

The microscopic dino-flagellates are forms of phytoplankton that use their whiplike tails to swim about in the ocean.

Like the producers, the herbivores of the oceanic zone are also tiny. The major primary consumers of this zone are the microscopic zooplankton. Among the zooplankton are many kinds of one-celled animals such as amebas, foraminiferans, and radiolarians. Even more abundant are tiny relatives of shrimps and lobsters called *copepods*. Copepods are probably the most important food source for the higher feeding levels.

The secondary consumers of the oceanic zone include many kinds of small fish that feed upon the copepods. So do the huge whalebone whales, which filter vast amounts of seawater, straining out the tons of copepods that a whale needs.

Larger fish, such as tuna, mackerel, and swordfish, are among the tertiary consumers. So are sharks and rays, squids, toothed whales, and even birds. Some birds, such as petrels and albatrosses, spend most of their lives hunting over the open sea, returning to land only to nest and breed. Seals, sea lions, and walruses hunt in the open sea.

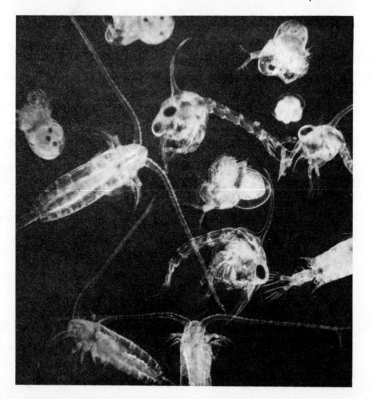

Figure 8–5

Tiny relatives of shrimps and crabs are the most abundant primary consumers of the ocean, depending on diatoms and dinoflagellates for their food supply.

Figure 8–6

The sea lion, the albatross, and the shark are all third-level consumers of the open ocean, feeding on small fish, the secondary consumers, which in turn depend on the organisms shown in Figure 8–5.

Ocean Life at Great Depths

We have been talking about the sunlit upper layers of the open ocean, where photosynthesis can go on. This layer is only several hundred feet deep at most. It can be much shallower where production of living material is heavy, and absorption of light is greater. All life in the ocean, at all depths, depends on this layer.

At the greater depths, where there is no light, there is no photosynthesis. There can be no producers. The first source of food must be the organic debris falling from above. Decomposition is slow in the cold deep water, and primary consumers can feed on the debris.

By towing nets at many depths, scientists have come to know a great deal about the zooplankton of the deep ocean, capturing small animals from the darkest, coldest deeps. However, very little is known about larger animals of the deeper waters. Large, free-swimming animals easily avoid towed nets. Underwater photography so far has not been entirely successful. Divers cannot penetrate very deep, and larger animals may avoid the few research submarines that can.

However, deep sea fish have been captured. Some have huge eyes adapted to the dim light that reaches the depths. Many have luminescent organs that produce their own light. Some have mouths and stomachs that can be expanded to enable them to swallow prey larger than themselves. Food is probably so scarce in these zones that such fish have to be able to take advantage of every possible meal. However, most of these "monsters" are very small, the largest being a few inches long.

Yet, the deeper waters have occasionally yielded giant squid, with bodies 15 to 20 feet long, with their longer tentacles adding another 20 to 30 feet. Sperm whales sometimes feed very deep and eat large squid.

There is life even on the ocean floor. Starfish, sea cucumbers and sea lilies (both of which are animals), worms, and shellfish live even at the greatest depths. Huge populations of bacteria live in the mud surface, acting as the chief decomposers for the ocean system.

Figure 8–7

The formidable "snout" on the angler fish shown at the right is probably a luminescent organ. What other adaptations for deep-sea life do these fish have?

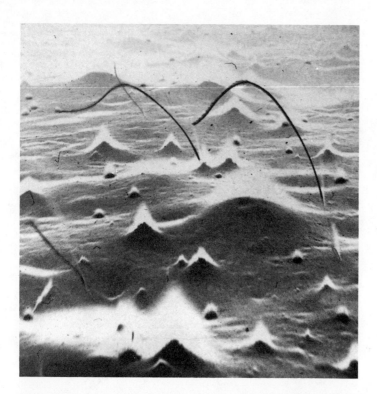

Figure 8–8

The photo of the ocean bottom at the left was taken at a depth of 295 feet by a special underwater camera called a benthograph. It shows many sea urchins, which appear as globular, light-colored bodies, and long sea whips. Burrowing worms have formed the cone-shaped mounds of sediment.

The bottom photo is an electron micrograph of material removed from the ocean bottom at 8500 feet. The shells of one-celled forms called foraminifera and radiolaria sink to the bottom and accumulate on the sea floor.

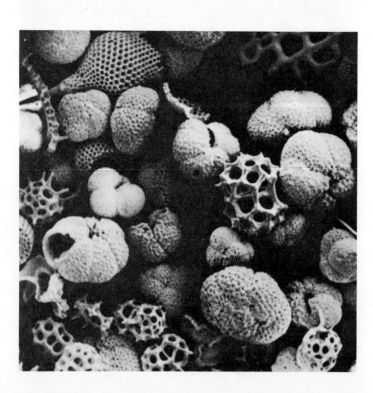

Shallow Water: The Near-Shore and Intertidal Zones

The life of the near-shore waters is generally more abundant than that of the open sea, especially on the bottom. In relatively shallow water, for one thing, the bottom dwellers are still in contact with producers. Here in the shallow water, as well as in the deep, the phytoplankton are the most important producers. Seaweeds grow in the shallows and are easily seen, but play a very small part in the lives of most animals.

As in the oceanic zone, the primary consumer level is chiefly made up of zooplankton. However, much of the zooplankton population in the near-shore zone is composed of the tiny larvae of organisms that will later grow up to become secondary consumers or bottom-dwellers. Larvae of worms, shellfish, snails, starfish, jellyfish, and even some fish make up sizeable portions of the zooplankton population. As they grow up, they take up life on the bottom or themselves begin to feed on the zooplankton.

Most of the secondary and tertiary consumers of the oceanic region also venture into the near-shore zone. In addition, there are many animals that seldom leave the shallower waters. These include many kinds of fish, sharks, and sea birds. The members of the herring family of fish—including sardines and anchovies—are *filter feeders*. They strain plankton from the water by use of specially developed "nets" in their gills. Salmon, mackerel, tuna, and bonitos are among the fish feeding on larger organisms in the near-shore zone.

The abundant bottom life of the near-shore zone varies according to whether the bottom is soft or rocky. On sandy or muddy bottoms, many forms of burrowing animals such as clams, snails, worms, shrimp, and crabs are found. Tiny algae may exist among the sand grains, but the larger seaweeds are rare on such shifting bottoms. On rocky bottoms, attached organisms such as seaweed, sea anemones, sea urchins, and corals are more common.

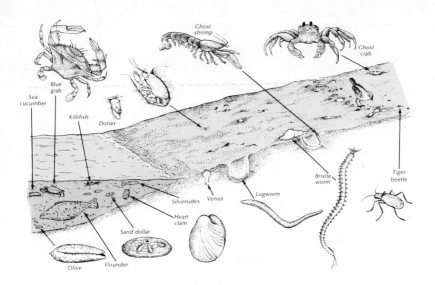

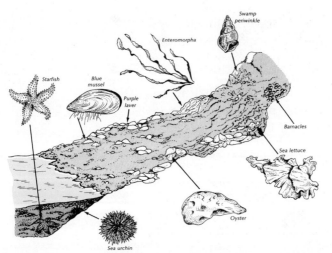

Figure 8–9

Characteristic zones of life on a sandy ocean beach (top) and a rocky shore (bottom) along the Atlantic coast. Note that burrowing forms are more common in sand, while clinging forms are more common on the rocky surface.

Crabs, lobsters, and starfish are predators moving about on the bottom. Flounders, rays, cod, haddock, and halibut are among the fish that feed chiefly on bottom dwellers.

The intertidal zone—the zone between the levels of high and low tide—is one of the most unusual environments for life on earth. Anything that lives here must survive the pounding of the surf during much of the day. It is exposed to sunlight and air and land predators at low tide, and to salt water and ocean predators at high tide. On rocky shores, this zone is often thickly covered with mussels, oysters, and barnacles. These shellfish are firmly attached to the rocks, helping them to resist the surf, and are protected from the extremes of temperature and dryness by their tightly-closing shells. On sandy shores, this zone is chiefly occupied by burrowing animals such as worms, sand fleas, and snails.

The organisms of the intertidal zone are hunted from both land and sea. Crabs and snails hunt in this zone much of the time. When the tide is in, flounders, killifish, silversides and other fish move in to feed. When the tide is out, shore birds and some animals move out onto the exposed rocks and sand to gather whatever food they can find.

Special Habitats

Rocky shores often include special habitats called *tidepools*. These are depressions in the rock, usually shallow, ranging from dishpan or bathtub-size to room-size. These are left uncovered but full of water and of life when the tide recedes. Tidepools harbor complex communities of animals, some of them free-moving, such as crabs and snails, and others (such as sea anemones) attached like plants. Tidepool animals are better able than most sea creatures to withstand rapid changes of temperature, salinity, and moisture conditions, or even exposure to air. In few other habitats can there be such a striking variety of life forms within a small space. Each pool is a separate "aquarium" bearing its own strikingly beautiful collection of plant and animal residents. Needless to say, tidepools can be fascinating to scientists and even to casual visitors to the seashore.

Other special environments exist in shallow bays and lagoons, tidal flats and marshes, and estuaries. Here the water may be nearly fresh or very brackish, currents are strong or nonexistent, and temperatures and water level may vary greatly from time to time. Some marine organisms and some land organisms are able to live in these specialized habitats, and some creatures adapted only for this environment are known.

Figure 8–10
Low tide in an intertidal zone off the coast of England. The rocks are thickly covered with a variety of seaweed. The bottom photograph is a detail of a tidepool, which is lined with an alga. The animals in the center are sea anemones, with seaweeds on either side and barnacles in the background. At the top and bottom right are limpets, mollusks distantly related to oysters.

Many animals of the near-shore zone spend the early part of their lives in the waters of estuaries, where abundant plankton and nutrients are washed into the sea. In some cases, these muddy river mouths play an important role in keeping up the populations of fish that men catch as adults out in the open ocean. These fish enter the estuaries to breed and lay their eggs, and the young fish live on the rich food of the river mouth for some weeks or months before entering the ocean. Some species, such as the salmon, swim far upstream to lay their eggs. For these species, the dredging of streams, building of dams, and dumping of sewage into the rivers has created great hazards. Even the dumping of clean but warm water by industries may make conditions unsuitable for the survival of the young fish.

One organism seriously threatened by estuary pollution is the oyster. Oysters are the most prominent members of the community living in river mouths. They cluster on rocks in the intertidal zone, or form great reefs of oysters cemented to the shells of past generations. They are filter feeders, straining their food from the plankton and organic debris washed down the river.

Because the oysters collect and concentrate the material in the river water, they are particularly affected by river pollution. In many river mouths where sewage and industrial waste has been dumped into the river upstream, oysters have largely disappeared. Even where the oysters have managed to survive, their flesh has such a high concentration of dangerous chemicals and bacteria that they cannot be eaten by humans. As an example, we may note that 18 million pounds of oysters were caught in the Middle Atlantic states in 1950; in 1965 the total catch was only 757,000 pounds in those states.

Figure 8–11

The oyster industry used to be an important economic activity in the Chesapeake Bay region, but pollution of river mouths has considerably reduced oyster yield there in the last 20 years.

Food from the Sea

As the human population has increased, food has become scarce. Many people have expressed hope that the sea can provide additional food within the next few decades. Seafood accounts for only a small percentage of the world's total food supply today. However, the present catch of over 50 million metric tons per year represents about one fifth of the world's meat protein supply. Doubling this catch would increase the available amount of animal protein by one fifth. This could have great benefits in countries where people do not have enough protein in their diet. Can the world's fish catch be increased? Couldn't more and better fishing boats catch more fish? This seems simple enough. It also looks very promising when you consider that almost all of the world's catch of fish is taken on only about 10 percent of the ocean's total surface area. To many people, increasing the catch looks like a simple matter of fishing the other 90 percent.

There is, as the saying goes, a catch to this. In fact there are several catches. First, almost all the fish production in the seas takes place within that 10 percent already being fished. In fact, half the total world production occurs in one tenth of 1 percent of the ocean area, in places where upwelling brings nutrients to the surface right along coasts. Total world fish production today is just over 240,000,000 metric tons per year. The open ocean accounts for only 160,000 metric tons.

Of this total production, scientists believe that 100 million metric tons could be available for sustained harvesting. Sustained harvesting means fishing in such a way as to be able to catch the same amount year after year. The rest of the fish have to be left as breeding stock and as steps in the food pyramids of those that are caught. A few optimistic scientists see a sustained catch of 150 million metric tons as possible eventually, provided all precautions are taken to protect breeding stock and pollution damage is held to a minimum.

Whether the annual harvest is to be 100 or 150 million metric tons, it cannot be that large today or tomorrow. Improved fishing techniques will have to be developed. The two tonnages represent only a doubling or a tripling of the amount of fish that were taken in 1970. Remember, this means increasing the world's animal protein supply by one or two fifths. But suppose all the proper techniques could be developed by the year 2000. By that time, the world human population is expected to be about double what it is now. The per person share of fish will be smaller than it is today.

Overfishing

Consider, also, the problem of overfishing. The example of the whales is a frightening one. These huge mammals are now thought to be among the most intelligent animals on earth. But they reproduce slowly, and their population was never very dense in the oceans. When man began to hunt the whales—seeking their meat and the oil from their blubber—he caused serious declines in whale populations.

Figure 8–12

The harpoon gun and steam-powered boats made it possible to capture whales such as the 90-foot blue whale shown as a carcass.

At first, whales were caught chiefly when they happened to become stranded in shallow water, or when dead bodies washed ashore. The first major whaling fleet began to hunt the Atlantic right whale during the sixteenth century. Soon the numbers of these whales had been so reduced that the fleets headed for northern waters to hunt the Greenland right whale during the seventeenth century. When those had nearly been exterminated, the eighteenth century whalers traveled south to catch the southern right whale and the sperm whale. The sperm whale industry was a major support of the economy of New England, reaching a peak of 729 American whaling ships in 1846. As the numbers of sperm whales began to decline, the whalers turned to the Pacific coast, where they slaughtered the Pacific gray whale in the lagoons where it bred and gave birth. It has been guessed that in 4 years the population of gray whales dropped from about 30,000 to less than 100 as a result of the whalers' efforts.

In the middle of the nineteenth century, petroleum began to replace whale oil as a fuel for lamps and stoves. Although whaling was no longer a major industry, it did not cease. In fact, other uses for whale oil (in foods, lubricants, and soaps) rapidly increased. The development of harpoons fired from guns and steam-powered ships made it possible to hunt the blue and finback whales, which had been too fast for the old sailing ships and hand-thrown harpoons. By 1900, whales were very scarce in most of the world's oceans, and the whalers turned to the Antarctic. Great factory ships were developed to process the whales far from shore stations. The untouched whale populations of the Antarctic and the new techniques caused the catch of whales to increase again, and around 1930 the total amount of whale oil harvested reached the highest level in history.

Soon after that, as the yearly catch again declined, it was realized that there was a serious danger that all of the whales in the world's oceans would be exterminated. Various attempts were made to set limits on the number of whales captured each year. Some countries have not respected these agreements, and the whaling industry has insisted upon limits much higher than those recommended by scientists. Use of sonar devices and helicopters to locate the whales has made hunting even more efficient in recent years. It now appears likely that at least some species, such as the blue whale, which is the largest animal that has ever lived on earth, will disappear from the earth entirely. Other species will survive only if some effective international agreement to halt or severely limit whaling is reached.

Mankind has never had a chance to find out what role the various whale species played in the ecology of the sea. It must have been important, because only a generation ago there were hundreds of thousands of these huge animals, and perhaps millions before that. How will all the food pyramids readjust themselves when the whales are gone? Nobody knows.

More people have depended on various kinds of true fish for food than ever depended on whales. The whale story is being repeated with many species of valuable fish. Recently developed techniques make possible catches undreamed of 20 years ago, but the result can be the destruction of a fishery. The entire British herring fishery was wiped out within a few years in the late 1960's. Stocks of sardines, salmon, cod, tuna, and plaice are now being overfished at similar rates. Today's efficient methods sometimes leave little or no breeding stock, and often destroy the breeding and feeding grounds for bottom-living fish.

Sea Farming

Some think that some method of "farming" the sea plants and animals, rather than simply hunting them, will provide a greatly increased yield of food. Farming of the sea faces many problems, however. The difficulties involved in simply moving freely about the ocean may be solved by modern technology. In fact, there is serious talk about cities on the ocean floor in the not-too-distant future. But there are other difficulties.

As we have seen, large plants are very rare in the sea. The large algae, or seaweeds, will grow only near the shore, in shallow water with a rocky bottom. Most such areas are already densely populated with seaweed, which is gathered for food in most parts of the world. Any major increase in plant farming would have to come through use of the phytoplankton as a human food source. The first major problem is that processing of 400 tons of seawater produces only 10 grams of protein from the plankton. Second, no one has yet succeeded in finding an economical way to turn the plankton into tasty food. Most efforts so far have resulted in a very fishy-tasting, stomach-turning paste or powder. Third, we would have to start practically from scratch in learning how to farm these sea plants in a way that would significantly increase the possible food yield. We do not know what kinds of fertilizers or nutrients they need. We do not know what other chemicals in the water are helpful or harmful. We do not know what other organisms act as pests and which ones are necessary to the survival of the entire community. In short, it is likely to take many years of study and experimentation before plankton can provide a major source of human food.

We may be able to increase our catch of fish by learning to farm them as domesticated animals, rather than hunting them in the wild as we now do. However, again, most of the problems of plankton growing must be solved in order to provide food for the domestic herds of fish. Further, all of the complex ecological needs of the fish must be discovered and provided for. We must keep in mind that in harvesting fish we are taking our food from the tops of the ocean food pyramids. It has been estimated that 10,000 pounds of diatoms are needed to produce one pound of tuna flesh at the top of the food pyramid.

There is some evidence that fish farming could increase our yield of seafood. In the natural oceans, estimated production of fish each year is about 5 to 100 pounds per acre. In seawater fish ponds, where such special food fish as milkfish and mullets are raised, yields of 150 to 500 pounds per acre have been reached, under very favorable conditions. With the use of fertilizer to increase diatom production, yields of 1,000 pounds per acre have been achieved in Formosa. This compares very favorably with the 250 pounds of cattle produced on grazing lands.

However, we have a lot to learn before we can produce such yields in very large commercial lakes, or in the sea itself. There is little sign today of the expensive and large-scale effort that would be needed to learn how to produce large amounts of food from the sea.

Finally, we should mention that in the sea—as in lakes—an overabundance of nutrients sometimes poses serious problems. When too much fertilizer is available, populations of dinoflagellates may become so dense that the ocean water looks like tomato soup—the so-called "red tides." In these dense concentrations, the plankton may produce waste products that poison fish and other forms of life in the sea. Such red tides have always occurred occasionally when natural nutrient concentrations become high for one reason or another. However, in recent years they seem to have become more frequent and more extensive, and to affect areas of the ocean that were seldom affected before. The fertilizers washed from rivers and sewage outlets into the sea seem to be the major cause.

The Threat of Pollution

The seas represent our greatest untapped resource. Man may make great use of the ocean ecosystem in the future. However, we are in grave danger of destroying that ecosystem unintentionally before we know what we are doing.

The ocean has long been used as a dumping place for radioactive materials, unwanted explosives, and general garbage. Some attempts to mine minerals from the sea floor have had to be abandoned because of the hazards posed by bombs and explosives dumped there or left over from military target practice. Jacques-Yves Cousteau reported that the first sight to greet his eyes when he reached the bottom on his first deep ocean dive in a diving saucer was a spread-out newspaper on the ocean floor!

Pollutants often do not spread uniformly through the oceans, but are concentrated by currents and eddies.

The outflow from warm rivers does not settle downward, but remains in the thin warm upper layer. Thus many of the pollutants dumped into rivers reach high concentrations in the very area where photosynthesis occurs. As we have seen, all of the production for the entire ocean ecosystem takes place in this zone. Any damage to the population of this zone is sure to have far-reaching effects on all ocean life.

We know that some pollutants are reaching dangerous levels in this zone. Since 1923, the lead content of the surface waters of the oceans has increased from a negligible amount to nearly 10 milligrams per cubic yard. All of this has apparently resulted from the addition of lead as an anti-knock ingredient in gasoline. Lead is known to be poisonous to many organisms, but we do not know if the present concentration is great enough to harm the plankton of the zone where photosynthesis occurs.

Even in the open sea, where we do not fish very much, pollution can be serious. It is now well known that DDT and its chemical relatives are everywhere in the ocean. These chemicals are found in the fat of seals and penguins in the Antarctic—thousands of miles from where any DDT has ever been used. The billions of copepods that form the bases of so many food chains are related to insects, which DDT was meant to kill. How will increasing amounts of DDT and similar chemicals in seawater affect them? Nobody yet knows.

Experiments have shown that DDT interferes with photosynthesis in diatoms and other marine algae. This is an accidental, unintended effect. DDT was not designed to have any effect on plants. If photosynthesis in the ocean decreases, food chains must of course be affected. So must the production of oxygen in the sea. About two thirds of the oxygen in the atmosphere came originally from marine plants. Only about one third has been contributed by land plants over the ages. What if this interference with photosynthesis by DDT increases in the sea? Besides, what effects do the weed killers washed into the sea have on marine plants? What effects will other man-made chemicals have? Just how much of how many different new chemicals are we putting into the sea? Nobody knows the answers to any of these questions.

One of the most common ocean pollutants today is oil. It comes from many sources. Used oil dumped on land finds its way into rivers and to the sea. Both oil refineries on land and tankers at sea have leaks or other accidents. From time to time we hear of spectacular oil spills that kill thousands of sea birds and leave miles of beaches blackened. But nowadays oil is on and in the sea all the time, just because so much is used and transported and discarded. Lumps of tar from petroleum have been found everywhere on the surface of the North Atlantic Ocean. This was not the case in the 1950's or early 1960's.

Figure 8–13

This oil-soaked Long Island beach and the gannet struggling for its life are only the more evident signs of ocean-wide oil pollution.

There is more to this problem than the visible tar and oil. The oil slowly breaks down in the sea, leaving its components. Some of these components are chemically similar to organic compounds that many sea organisms take in as food. But they lack food value. Biologists fear that other components may resemble the hormones that regulate reproducing behavior amoung certain sea organisms. Some compounds may paralyze the organs of taste or smell of marine animals, making it difficult for them to migrate, locate prey, or carry on other activities that depend on the senses.

In short, we are damaging the ocean ecosystem in many ways. As yet, we know so little about this ecosystem that we can say little about the long-term effects. We do not know whether we have yet done irreversible damage to the life of the sea. We do know that many of man's activities are very probably doing serious damage, and that the damage is likely to increase.

The oceans may yet be a rich frontier, with new resources for an increasing human population. But this frontier will have to be cared for, like a cherished garden. Its resources must be cultivated wisely.

Test Yourself

1. What is meant by upwelling in the sea? What causes it?
2. What two kinds of plants serve as the basis of nearly all food chains in the ocean?
3. What kind of animal seems to be the most important primary consumer in ocean food chains? What surprisingly large animals depend directly on this kind?
4. Give two reasons why sea life is usually most abundant near coasts, or in the shallows and bottoms directly along the shore.
5. How much of an effect would doubling or tripling the tonnage of fish caught today have on the world animal protein supply by the year 2000?
6. Describe some advantages to sea farming. Describe some difficulties or problems.

7. How would you relate the tale about The Goose That Laid the Golden Egg to present attempts to get more food from the oceans?
8. In the United States, fish makes up only a small percentage of the animal protein in the average human diet. This proportion is much lower than the average for the world human population. Discuss why this is so.
9. What might be the effects on the human population if pesticides, weed-killers, or other pollution reduced the populations of plankton plants in the oceans?
10. Why do you suppose seaweeds are not important in the total food web of the ocean (though they may be important locally)?
11. Many fish of the ocean surface zone are colored blue on their backs, and white below. Also, many of the zooplankton are transparent. What influences in the environment might have led to development of such characteristics?

Land Ecosystems

The Variety of Land Environments

Land provides a much greater variety of physical environments than do the oceans or bodies of fresh water. As we saw earlier, such conditions as temperature tend to remain stable in the ocean, over wide areas and over long periods of time. On land, temperatures vary greatly, not only from season to season, but from day to night. In a desert, the temperature may fall at night to below freezing and then rise during the day to more than 125°F.

The growth of land plants is affected by the amount of moisture locally available and, needless to say, water ecosystems have no moisture problem. The many possible combinations of temperature and moisture conditions, frequency of rain and snow, soil type, altitude, and lengths of days, nights, and seasons make for a very wide variety of environments on land. Such a variety often exists even over a small area. Plants and animals in a valley will be different from those on the mountains on either side. Also, one mountain slope may be humid and forest-covered, while another is dry, supporting only sparse grass and shrub. The kinds of ecosystems the valley and mountains will have depend on whether they are in the tropics or nearer the polar regions, whether near or far from an ocean, and so on.

Mankind has a serious stake in understanding the great variety of the world's ecosystems, and what the variety means. This is especially important in a hungry world in which the population is growing rapidly, and much of the farmland is being paved over. It has happened again and again that a farming technique that worked well in the United States or Europe failed when applied in other places. Crops that grew very well in one place refused to grow in another, even though conditions seemed similar. Obviously, we need to know more about what an ecosystem is, how ecosystems differ, and what their similarities are.

Major Regions of the Earth

For convenience, geographers and other scientists have developed several different ways of grouping land communities, or ecosystems. Each system is useful for certain kinds of studies. All are used at one time or another in the field of ecology. We shall look briefly at a few of these systems, and then explore one in greater depth.

Students of plant and animal species long ago recognized that the land areas of the earth could be divided into several major regions. Each region contained a large number of species not found elsewhere. Only a few species (including man) were common in all regions. The most distinctive of these regions is the Australian region, which includes Tasmania and New Guinea. This part of the world has apparently had no land connection to the other parts for many millions of years. Reptiles, amphibians, and freshwater fish are rare in the Australian region. The mammals of this region are classed as *marsupials*. Typified by the kangaroo, the marsupial mother carries her young in a pouch in her abdominal skin. The milk glands and nipples are inside the pouch. The young are born at a stage when they are so small, undeveloped, and helpless that they could not survive outside the pouch. The marsupials occupy most of the mammalian niches in this region. The more familiar *placental* mammals, which do not give birth until the young are better developed and so need no pouch, were absent from the Australian region until brought there by man. Marsupials

are a very primitive mammal type, and do not compete well with placentals. For this reason marsupials are not common in the rest of the world, though they exist; the oppossum of North America is a marsupial.

The other regions are less distinctive, each sharing a fair number of species with its neighbors. South America is the only other region that shares very few animal types with its neighbors. Some have argued that there are really only three major animal regions: the Australian, the South American, and the rest of the world.

These divisions are not very useful to the ecologist, for the ecosystems are similar in all regions. For example, large areas of grassland occur in each region. In each grassland community, there are large grazing animals filling the important niches at the primary consumer level. In each region, different species fill this niche. In America, bison and pronghorn antelope grazed the great plains of the Midwest. In South Africa, great herds of a variety of species, including antelope and zebras, spread over the grasslands. In Europe and Asia, wild horses and donkeys fill this role. In Australia, the large kangaroos grazed on the grasslands until man replaced them with his cattle and sheep. Such species, which occupy similar niches in different regions, are said to be *ecological equivalents*.

The *biome* is most often used by biologists. Each biome is distinguished by a certain form of climax community of plants and animals, and a certain sequence of temporary communities that succeed one another until the climax community is reached. These communities may differ greatly in individual species from region to region. However, the general structure of the communities, and the nature of the available niches, are very similar around the world.

Biomes do not have sharp borders, although they are usually drawn in that way on a map. They do not begin or end suddenly. Each biome gradually blends into its neighbors. For example, between the deciduous forest biome of the eastern United States and the coniferous forest biome of Canada, there is a region of mixed forests, containing both deciduous hardwoods and coniferous trees. In this chapter, we shall look briefly at the major biomes of the world, particularly those in North America.

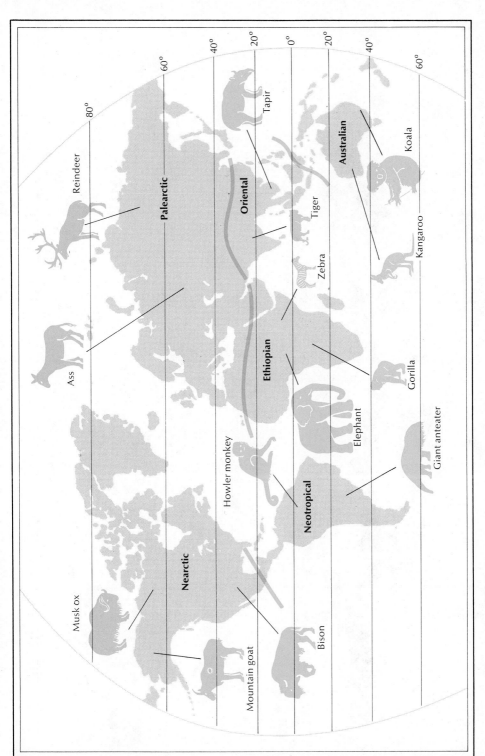

Figure 9–1 One way of classifying communities of the earth is by their distinctive animals. The map shows one such division into six so-called biogeographical realms. Why is this classification system not particularly useful to ecologists?

Figure 9–2 The biome is the community classification most convenient to ecologists. A biome is a large geographical area with a distinct climate and identified primarily by its climax vegetation. All biomes are ecosystems but an ecosystem is not

Tundra

Northern conifer forest

Temperate deciduous forest

Temperate grassland

Chaparral (temperate scrub forest)

Desert

Tropical rain forest

Tropical deciduous forest

Tropical scrub forest

Tropical grassland

Mountains

The Tundra Biome

Along the northern border of North America, Europe, and Asia is a region of very low temperatures and slight precipitation. Much of the soil remains frozen throughout the year, though the upper few inches melt for a few months during the summer. Temperatures are high enough to permit the growth of plants only during about 60 days of each year. Although few species are able to withstand this harsh environment, and the community is a simplified one, life is by no means rare in this *arctic tundra* biome.

A permanently frozen layer in the soil (called *permafrost*) prevents rainfall or meltwater from soaking into the ground. Thus, during the short summer, the low parts of the tundra are covered with lakes and bogs. Most of the surface is covered by a thick mat of low plants, including mosses, lichens, rushes, grasses, and low shrubs. Because of the slow growth rates at low temperatures, and the short period of thawing, the plants do little to change the nature of the soil. Only the hardiest pioneer plants survive here. The plants must withstand high winds and freezing temperatures. Few bacteria or other decomposers can function in these temperatures, and their work is very slow. Undecayed vegetation often forms a thick mat intertwined with the living plants. The soil is poor in organic matter and in the nitrates, phosphates, and other minerals that the decomposers can liberate in richer soils.

Like the plant species, the animal species are few in number when compared to other biomes. However, there is far more life here than one might expect. As soon as the surface thaws, a variety of water birds, sandpipers, and plovers arrive from the south to nest in the ponds and bogs. They head south again before the ice returns.

Ground squirrels hibernate in their burrows through the long winter. In May they emerge and mate. The young are born in mid-June. By the beginning of October, the young have reached adult size, and all of the ground squirrels return to their burrows for the winter hibernation. Other animals of the tundra remain active through the winter.

Primary consumers include lemmings, ground squirrels, and caribou. Feeding on these are arctic foxes, snowy owls, wolves, and people. Many of these animals have white coats in winter, which make them hard to see against the winter snow. They have heavy layers of fat and thick fur or feathers for protection against the cold. The lemmings and other rodents, and small predators such as weasels, tunnel beneath the snow, which insulates them from the severe cold. The caribou move southward, even out of the tundra, during the winter. Most of the plant-eating birds leave the tundra during the winter.

During the winter, food chains are short. If one population is depleted for any reason, there is little food available for its natural predators. As we saw earlier, population explosions and crashes are not unusual in the tundra, particularly among the lemmings.

In the brief summer, the migratory birds arrive and the caribou return from the south. The ground squirrels emerge from their hibernation. Insects and snails that spent the winter as pupae or eggs emerge. In mid-July,

Figure 9–3

Small ponds form during the short summer in the arctic tundra of Alaska, as the water is unable to soak through the permafrost. Note the marsh marigolds around the pond and the ice on the larger lake in the background.

the air is full of flies and mosquitoes. Now the food web is more complex. Longer food chains and alternate sources of food exist, and extreme population changes are far less likely.

In the high mountains farther to the south, there is a similar environment of low temperatures, low precipitation, and short growing season. Permafrost is found only at the very highest elevations, and bogs are found only in the high mountain meadows. Water erosion plays a more prominent part in shaping the land. However, the communities of these high mountains are similar to those of the northern tundra. Such areas are called the *alpine tundra* biome.

The plants of the alpine tundra get more light than those of the arctic. However, they must contend with even stronger winds, greater changes of temperature, and deeper winter snow cover. Only about one-fifth of the alpine tundra plant species are also found in the arctic tundra. Lichens and mosses are found chiefly on the rocks in the mountains, though they form a thick ground cover in the arctic. In the alpine tundra, low plants with thick outer coverings and scaly surfaces form cushions or mats over much of the ground. Within this mat, the temperature may be 20° higher than that outside, and many insects live within the mat. The windiest spots are largely barren rock. The more protected meadows look much like the bogs and other areas of the arctic tundra, though the plant species are largely different.

Primary consumers include pocket gophers, voles, marmots, mountain goats and sheep, and elk. During the winter, the elk and sheep move to lower parts of the mountain. The marmot hibernates. The voles and gophers eat the roots of plants that lie beneath the snow.

Most of the predators of the alpine tundra are visitors from the lower slopes. Eagles, vultures, hawks, foxes, weasels, and pumas (mountain lions) all travel up to hunt the residents of the high mountains, though most of them make their permanent homes in the warmer lower slopes.

Flies and mosquitoes are rare in the high mountains, but butterflies, grasshoppers, beetles, and springtails are common. Flying insects have a difficult time in the high winds. Thus most of the insects of the alpine tundra are wingless. Even the butterflies make only short flights very close to the ground.

Population explosions and crashes, particularly among the rapidly-breeding voles, are not uncommon in the alpine tundra. Parasites, diseases, and the harsh conditions of the environment seem to be the chief limiting factors on populations, for predators are scarce, particularly in winter.

The Coniferous Forest Biome

The northern evergreen forests stretch in a broad band just south of the Arctic tundra across North America, Asia, and Europe. This biome is also a region of short summers and long, cold winters. However, conditions are not as harsh as those in the tundra, and precipitation is somewhat greater. Milder winds, longer growing season, greater precipitation, and the lack of permafrost enable the needle-leaved evergreen trees (conifers) to thrive in this biome, and they dominate the forests. Spruce, pine, fir, hemlock, and cedar make up the coniferous forests, with some birch and willow here and there. Most hardwoods and other deciduous trees are unable to survive in the poor soil and cold climate of this biome.

Much of this area was covered by sheet glaciers during the Ice Ages, and lakes and bogs fill the low spots in the glacially-carved landscape. Because of the dense tree cover throughout the year, the coniferous forest is a place of deep shade, mild winds, and somewhat lessened temperature changes. The soil is low in iron and lime, and unsuitable for many kinds of plants. The poor soil and dense shade permit few smaller trees or shrubs to grow under the conifers. The litter of conifer needles seems to be an unsuitable environment for most of the larger animals that live in or on the soil, but the smaller insects and microscopic decomposers are common.

Squirrels, birds, and insects feed upon the cones and needles of the trees. Other primary consumers, such as the moose and snowshoe-hare, feed in large part on the broad-leaved plants formed in gaps in the coniferous forest. Deer are abundant, finding excellent winter shelter in the forest. Elk from the higher mountains and caribou from the tundra enter the coniferous forest for the winter. Predators include hunting birds, wolves, pumas, black bears, foxes, weasels, wolverines, and lynxes.

Although populations may fluctuate in cycles of several years, the extreme and sudden population explosions of the tundra seldom happen in the forest. The food web is more complex, and most animals are able to find several sources of food. Where the forest is dominated by only one or two species of tree, outbreaks of insect pests that feed on that species may cause serious damage.

Coniferous forests also grow on the higher slopes of mountain ranges, just below the alpine tundra. The area between alpine tundra and coniferous forest is called the *Krummholz*, or "crooked wood." It is a band of dwarfed, wind-twisted trees, with tundra vegetation in the open spaces.

The Temperate Deciduous Forest Biome

Deciduous forests have been described in earlier chapters. Their biome has moderate temperatures, but with cold winters, warm summers, and abundant rainfall evenly spaced through the year. A rich organic soil is produced by the activity of the plant and animal community. Eastern North America, most of Europe, the tip of South America, and parts of Japan and Australia were once covered by deciduous forests. Logging and clearing have greatly reduced the extent of these forests today.

The fall of the tree leaves in winter subjects the forest floor to greater variations of light, temperature, and wind. However, the greater light, particularly in winter, permits the development of one or more strata of undergrowth.

The deciduous forest provides a rich variety of habitats and niches, and an abundance of plants and animals thrive here. The climax communities are complex and stable, with large population fluctuations very rare.

To the north, the deciduous forest blends into the

coniferous forest in a wide band of mixed hardwood–conifer forests. As we saw in an earlier chapter, the pine forests of the southeastern United States are a stage in succession. In the absence of forest fires or constant logging, they are succeeded by a deciduous forest.

In addition to the broad zones of deciduous forest shown in Figure 9-1, there are zones of deciduous forest on the lower slopes of most mountains.

Grasslands

Where temperatures are moderate, but rainfall is too sparse to support the growth of trees, areas of grassland are found. These great prairies, or plains, occur largely in the interiors of continents. They have different local names: the Great Plains in America, the steppes in Russia, the veldt in South Africa, and the pampas in South America.

At one time, grasslands covered nearly half of the land area of the world. However, man learned to domesticate grazing animals of the grassland for meat and milk, and to cultivate grasses as grain crops. Most of the grasslands are now farmlands, or deserts created by man's careless disruption of the ecosystem.

Figure 9–4

Before they were destroyed by the European peoples, bison used to roam the grasslands of the western United States. They formed the basis of the economy of many Indian tribes, providing meat, dung for fuel, and pelts for clothing.

Trees do not grow well in the grasslands because of the low rainfall, occasional severe dry spells (droughts), and the abundance of grazing animals that eat saplings. The grasses form a thick network of roots through the upper foot or so of soil, and less thick root networks extend to depths of 3 feet or more. This root network holds the soil firmly in place, and during the winter, may represent the largest bulk of the plant biomass.

Above the ground, the taller grasses reach heights of 5 to 8 feet during the fall. Shorter grass species, wild mustard and other herbs reach a height of about 2 to 4 feet. The ground layer (1.5 feet or less in height) is made up of buffalo grass, wild strawberry, mosses, dandelions, and various wildflowers.

A thick layer of plant remains forms on the ground. The lower part of this layer, partially decayed and broken up, is called *mulch*. At the bottom of the mulch layer, where moisture is concentrated and decomposers are active, the mulch is converted into a rich soil.

Insects and other invertebrate animals live among all these plants in huge numbers and varieties. Earthworms and ants are abundant in the soil. Beetles and spiders live in the mulch and litter. Grasshoppers, crickets, leaf-hoppers, spittlebugs, and hundreds of other insect species live in the grass tops during the summer.

The primary consumers are a rich variety of mammals. Pocket gophers, prairie dogs, deer mice, jack rabbits, ground squirrels, prairie chickens, meadowlarks, and grouse were among the common small herbivores of the American prairies. Ecological equivalents exist in the other grasslands of the world. Most of these small animals live in burrows—either digging their own or taking over those of other species—or are swiftly running or hopping creatures.

Large grazing animals are characteristic of the grassland biome. In America, great herds of bison and pronghorn antelopes roamed the prairies. In most grasslands, the large grazing mammals live in herds, which afford protection against predators.

In America, the predators include coyotes, bobcats, kit foxes, badgers, hawks, owls, and snakes. These feed chiefly on the smaller animals, but coyotes occasionally band together to hunt weaker or younger members of the grazing herds. Wolves and pumas once hunted the larger animals of the plains, though man has now driven them out. Man has also replaced bison and antelope with cattle and sheep.

The grasses survive the occasional droughts, either by becoming dormant or by drawing water from deep roots. During dry periods that last several years, some of the dominant species may be greatly reduced in population, while more drought-resistant species take advantage of brief rainstorms or cool spells to spread over the land. When the drought is over, the composition of the plant community soon returns to the climax stage.

The herds of wild grazing animals seem to have caused little damage to the grasslands. The herds traveled widely, seldom grazing for long at any one place. Their numbers were kept in check by wolves, coyotes, and hunting tribes of humans.

Prairie dogs played an important role in maintaining the short-grass prairies of the drier regions. These little animals clip off the larger grasses for great distances around their burrows, and eat or cut down any shrubs in the area. Their activity apparently helped to maintain a variety of plants against the strong competition of the taller grasses, and was very important in keeping shrubs from invading the grassland.

In most parts of the world, the rich and complex grassland community has been replaced by a very much simplified tame community for raising grains or grazing cattle. Even constant application of pesticides and fertilizers has not prevented fairly frequent population crashes in this unstable ecosystem. When things get totally out of control, a man-made desert may result. This problem is not new. There is evidence that much of the desert land in northern Africa was created by the same kinds of land mismanagement of ancient civilizations. Anyone who visits the barren and rocky hills of Greece today may find it hard to believe that this was once rich farmland supporting a great civilization.

Deserts

Deserts are regions of very low rainfall, or of rainfall scattered very unevenly through the year with long dry spells. In the dry air, temperatures drop sharply at night and reach great heights during the day. Only in the central Sahara and the northern Chilean deserts is rainfall almost entirely lacking. In these deserts, and in others where the soil contains large amounts of salt, there is little or no life. Most deserts have a sparse covering of vegetation, however, and a surprising abundance of animal life.

The desert plants are chiefly of three types. First, there are those, like the cactus, that store water in their tissues and have thick waxy skins to prevent water loss by evaporation. Second, there are the shrubs with roots

Figure 9–5

The prickly pear cactus in the foreground and the giant sajuaro are abundant in the desert of the American southwest.

reaching tens or hundreds of feet down into the soil for water, and with the ability to drop their leaves and survive in a dormant state during long dry spells. Third, there are the wildflowers and grasses that grow swiftly after a rain, bloom, produce seed, and die, all in a space of a few weeks. The seeds of these short-lived plants can survive for years, and will sprout only when moisture and temperature conditions are just right.

Desert plants are widely spaced, with great stretches of bare ground between them. The ground is briefly covered by the wildflowers for a short time in the spring and again in the fall. At other times of the year, close inspection may reveal a thin scattering or crust of algae, lichens, and mosses on the sand or rocks. However, the lack of water sharply limits the amount of photosynthesis that can be carried out, and the productivity of deserts is very low.

Animals also find survival difficult in the desert. Most of the species that live there have special adaptations to conserve water. Few desert species of plants or animals are able to survive in other biomes. Apparently, they are unable to compete with the inhabitants of those ecosystems, except where lack of water handicaps the other species.

Insects and reptiles have thick outer coverings that minimize water loss through evaporation. They have nearly dry feces and excrete a dried concentrate of urine, losing little water in that way. They are also able to with-stand temperature extremes, though they may become dormant in order to do so.

Most of the desert mammals live in burrows. There conditions are relatively cool and moist during the day. They emerge at night to gather food. Many are able to produce extremely concentrated urine, and do not sweat. With these water conservation measures, some, such as the kangaroo rat, are able to survive on the water produced during the digestion of dry foods, and never need to drink water. Some become dormant during periods of extreme heat or drought. It has been suggested that the large ears of the desert foxes and rabbits serve primarily to radiate body heat.

Many insects survive the dry period as eggs or pupae.

After the rains, as the wildflowers spring up, the desert is suddenly alive with bees, wasps, grasshoppers, butterflies, moths, beetles, crickets, and flies. Ants are active during much of the year.

Desert predators include coyotes, foxes, various small cats, skunks, badgers, snakes, hawks, owls, and vultures. Among the other typical inhabitants of the American deserts are the kangaroo rats, jack rabbits, peccaries ("wild pigs"), rattlesnakes, Gila monsters, horned lizards ("horned toads"), tarantulas, and road runners.

Kangaroo rat

Deserts provide some of the most striking examples of ecological equivalents. The cactuses of American deserts have their equivalents in the euphorbias of African deserts, which look much the same but belong to an entirely different family of plants. Every desert in the world has a small, seed-eating, burrowing, hopping animal similar to the American kangaroo rat. In Africa and Asia there are gerbils and jerboas. The hamster of Asia fills a similar niche. Even in the Australian desert, a small hopping marsupial called the mouse kangaroo looks much the same and makes his living in the same way.

Gerbil

In some areas, desert soil is reasonably rich in nutrients. Only the lack of water prevents the growth of plants from other biomes. In such areas, man has produced productive farmland by bringing in water through irrigation systems. Where these systems draw on the deep pools of underground water beneath the desert itself, they seem doomed to a short productive life. The desert groundwater has accumulated over centuries, and such irrigation uses up the water much more quickly than it is replaced. In addition, the high evaporation rate in the dry desert air leads to a rapid accumulation of salts in the soil. To prevent this, additional amounts of water must be used to flush the salts off the land.

Hamster

Many desert irrigation projects are now underway or being planned. Some of them call for bringing in water from outside the desert. However, the deserts of the Middle East are scattered with the remains of ancient irrigation systems abandoned long ago. Some ecologists wonder if man understands the special hazards of the desert well enough to be as successful there as its natural inhabitants have been.

Mouse kangaroo

Chaparral Biome

Where annual rainfall is low, with long and dry summers, and mild and rainy winters, a special community exists. Called *chaparral* in the southwestern United States and *maquis* is the Mediterranean region, this biome is dominated by tall shrubs and dwarf trees about 5 to 10 feet tall. In California and Arizona, mesquite, manzanita, and small oak trees make up most of the chaparral plant population. In Australia, eucalyptus trees and shrubs dominate similar environments. (The eucalyptus, brought to California by man, is thriving so well that it crowds out many native species.)

There is little undergrowth beneath the shrubs, but the ground is thickly littered with the brittle branches and leaves of the chaparral brush. During the rainy season, mule deer and a great variety of birds live in the shrubs Lizards, chipmunks, wood rats, rabbits, and many insects also are a part of the chaparral community. Predators are chiefly foxes, coyotes, hawks, owls, and other visitors from other biomes nearby who enter the chaparral to hunt during the rainy season.

As the rains stop, the brush becomes very dry and brittle. The deer and birds move north or up into the mountains to find fresher greenery. The smaller animals and insects also seem less abundant, and the predators seek better hunting elsewhere. In the fall, fires spread with incredible swiftness through the litter of branches and dry shrubs. In the past, such fires were set by lightning in fall rainstorms or by the Indians. Today, efforts are usually made to prevent fires in the chaparral. However, year by year the pile of combustible litter grows thicker. Sooner or later, a carelessly tossed match or cigarette, or a lightning strike, is sure to set off a fire, and it is even fiercer and more rapid in its spread because of the delay.

The fires apparently played a major role in this ecosystem. Many of the shrubs have seeds that sprout only when scarred and burned. After the fire, grasses and wildflowers spring up at the first rain. The actions of these plants on the rich organic ashes left by the fire returns most of the nutrients that had been locked in the brush and litter back to the ground. The new shrubs grow quickly, crowding out the grasses. Within a decade or two, the chaparral community is restored.

Where the fires become too extensive—which often happens where fires have been prevented for many years—and a huge area is burnt over, the first rains may produce major floods before the covering of grass can spring up. In the heavy bursts of rain typical of this region, great torrents of muddy water may pour off the unprotected hills to flood the lowlands. These floods have caused major disasters in cities such as Los Angeles, which is built in the lowlands and stream channels (dry through most of the year) at the base of chaparral-covered hills.

Figure 9–6
Typical southern California chaparral shown after devastation by fire and flood.

It is this chaparral biome that has spread out into some of the grassland area where man has interfered with some of the natural limits to shrub growth. The chaparral community is generally regarded by man as an undesirable one. Man commonly attempts to replace it by grasslands or forest. However, it appears that most of this area is too dry for the forest community, but too moist to permit grasses to compete successfully with the shrubs. Because most of the area consists of steep hills and canyons, irrigated farming is impractical. Thus, unused areas of chaparral remain even in the midst of Los Angeles, where vacant land is very scarce.

Tropical Rain Forest Biome

The greatest variety of life, the most complex and stable ecosystems, exist in the warm regions of high rainfall near the equator. These rain forests or jungles of South and Central America, central Africa, and southeast Asia receive more than 80 inches of rain per year. The temperature difference between winter and summer is smaller than that between night and day. Rains come in sudden and powerful deluges.

There is a great variety of plant and animal life from place to place in the rain forest, but the general characteristics are the same almost everywhere. The trees are broad-leaved evergreens, tall and shallow-rooted. Climbing vines and smaller trees provide a rich vegetation at almost every level beneath the tall trees. So little light filters through this thick cover that small plants on the ground are quite sparse, except in clearings.

There is an incredible variety of species—both plant and animal—in the rain forest. It has been said that there are more different species in a few acres of rain forest than in all of Europe. Tens of thousands of niches exist in this complex ecosystem, and each seems to be filled. Stratification is particularly well developed in the rain forest.

Bats and birds hunt insects in the air above the trees. In the upper branches, birds, bats, monkeys, opossums, and a variety of other mammals feed on leaves, fruit, nectar, and insects. Other birds, bats, and gliding mammals flit among the trunks below. Monkeys, iguanas, geckos, chameleons, snakes, and others move up and down the trunks and vines to feed on fruits and insects. Larger mammals and some birds roam the ground or climb the lower trunks and vines, feeding on plants or the abundant animal life. A great variety of tiny animals live on the ground, including both primary and secondary consumers. Termites and fruits are probably the most important food sources for many of the inhabitants.

Although many of the plants and animals of the rain forest have colorings that appear gaudy and conspicuous in the zoo or the botanical garden, they are well camouflaged in the lush profusion of the rain forest. Most of the mammals are hidden away during the day, or unseen in the thick canopy of the upper trees. There are many creatures whose forms mimic leaves, twigs, animal droppings, flowers, or which simply blend into the plants or ground litter on which they rest.

The very lushness of the vegetation and the huge variety of species makes it extremely difficult to get any over-all picture of the rain forest. Although many thousands of species have been catalogued, and volumes written on their behavior and habits, we still are far from a complete understanding of this ecosystem.

Figure 9–7

In this tropical rain forest of Puerto Rico, the large fernlike trees are cycads, which are primitive conifers that were abundant all over the earth during the period when coal was being formed.

Where rain forests have been removed, they return slowly or not at all. In many cases, they are replaced by a very different forest of softwood trees. In some areas, where the rain forest was cleared to open up new land for farming, the soil exposed to the effects of rain and sunlight quickly turned into a solid, cementlike coating that would not support any plant life.

Although the rain forest is of little economic value to modern man, ecologists are very anxious to preserve it against the onslaughts of civilization. It represents the most complex ecosystem and the greatest variety of land species found on earth. For this reason, it is an ideal laboratory for the study of the processes of natural selection and adaptation. It may be of great importance to understand why this ecosystem, so stable in its natural form, is so thoroughly destroyed by disruption.

Having looked at the different kinds of biomes and all their special conditions, it is easy to see why opening up new land is not always a simple, efficient, or permanent solution to problems caused by loss of old farmland or by overpopulation.

With this background, we can now return to the problems of man as a member of the ecosystem with exceptional powers to modify and possibly destroy that ecosystem. In the remaining chapters, we turn chiefly to problems of human ecology.

Test Yourself

1. Why are the animal communities of the Australian region strikingly different from those of other regions?
2. What is meant by the term ecological equivalents? (Name some examples.)
3. What is the main thing that distinguishes one land biome from another?
4. What do you suppose is the main influence that governs whether a forest, a grassland, or a desert will occupy a given part of a temperate region?

5. Why do attempts to make new farmland by clearing off areas of tropical rain forest usually fail?

6. Which biome represents man's natural habitat? Why has man been so unusually successful in surviving in almost every biome?

7. Almost all of the naturally suitable farmland in the world is now in use. To supply food for the increasing human population, three major solutions have been suggested: (1) irrigate desert lands to make farming possible; (2) increase productivity of present farmland through use of fertilizers, better control of pests, and development of more efficient crops; and (3) make better use of the food resources of the oceans. Discuss the advantages and the difficulties of each solution. How much do you think each will contribute to the prevention of food shortages in the coming decades?

8. Why are the ecosystems of the tropical regions so much more complex than those of the arctic regions? What are the advantages and disadvantages for the survival of the ecosystem of such complexity? Is there any advantage to man in maintaining the variety of biomes and ecosystems that exists on earth? Can the analogy be extended to human social systems? That is, what are the effects of diversity and complexity of habitats and niches in a social or political grouping of people?

9. Discuss the similarities and differences among typical food webs in each of the major biomes.

10. It has been suggested that the rain forest is in some ways similar to the ocean ecosystem, with most photosynthesis occurring in the upper layer and the inhabitants of the bottom layers living on organic debris from above. How close does this comparison seem to you? What are the differences?

Conservation of Natural Resources

The Conservation Movement

There was a conservation movement in the United States long before people were aware of the science of ecology. The conservationists reached the first peak of their influence during the time of President Theodore Roosevelt at the beginning of this century. The concern at that time was largely a reaction to the incredible destruction of natural resources during the early history of this nation.

Within a few centuries, many of the riches of this vast continent had been seriously depleted. Huge forests had been leveled, careless farming had destroyed countless acres of fertile soil, and many of the native plants and animals of North America were threatened with extinction. Our young nation hardly noticed the destruction. There always seemed to be more untouched wilderness to the west. If the old land was ruined, it always seemed possible to find new resources at the frontier.

As the frontier disappeared, some people began to realize that some lands should be protected, lest all be ruined. The state of California gained ownership of Yosemite Valley in 1864. In 1872 Yellowstone National Park was created to preserve another natural wonder. In 1890 parts of the Sierra Nevada forests and redwood groves, including Yosemite, were added to the national park system. In 1891, a system of national forest reserves was authorized to protect some of the remaining forests from lumbering and clearing. Local states passed some laws to protect wildlife.

Yet these were small steps in comparison to the destruction that was occurring at the same time. The lumbermen had slashed their way across the continent, felling more than half of the available wood in the nation, and clearing some 200 million acres of former forest land. Hunting and destruction of natural habitats had nearly eliminated the pronghorn antelope, egret, heron, beaver, wolf, and many other species. The millions of bison that once roamed the forests and plains were nearly extinct. The flocks of billions of passenger pigeons that had darkened the skies over the eastern forests had been slaughtered for meat. The last passenger pigeon died in 1914. Heath hens, wild parakeets, and some species of elk also became extinct. Only a few grizzly bears were left, in the most hidden forests.

Figure 10–1

The passenger pigeon, which used to be killed for food, has been extinct since 1914. Nearly extinct species today include the whooping crane, the cheetah, the Bengal tiger, the white rhinoceros, and the monkey-eating eagle.

The national parks and preserves helped to conserve some of the dwindling land and wildlife resources. Stricter game laws; national, state, and local laws and game wardens; national agencies appointed to oversee natural resources; private organizations such as the Audubon Society and the Sierra Club—all of these played a part in conservation activity during the first part of this century. However, even their best efforts seemed unable to do more than slow the pace of destruction. After all, which was more important, a pretty forest or a new high-way? Those who wanted to save the natural environment seemed to be sentimentalists, hanging onto remnants of a long-vanished past and obstructing progress.

Over the past decade or so, the impact of the ecology movement has begun to change the picture. It now seems clear that conservation is not merely a matter of preserving a few pretty remnants of the past. Instead, it may be a matter of life or death for the human species. The problem is not merely conservation of resources; it is a problem of preserving a liveable environment.

Natural Resources

Natural resources are those things in our environment that we need. Our idea of what should be included may change from time to time. Neanderthal man may have regarded obsidian rock as a most important natural resource, while oil oozing from the ground would have been only a nuisance. Today our opinions might be just the opposite. Some natural resources, such as the air we breathe, have been so readily available that people didn't even think of them as resources. The list of natural resources for a sparrow or for a fox might be quite differ-ent from our own. Usually, when we speak of natural resources, we mean the things that *people* need.

Some resources are provided by the ecosystem in a steady supply, if we don't use them too hastily or damage the ecosystem too badly. Plants and animals can be taken for food and other purposes, and new plants and animals can grow to take their places. Supplies of air and water are recycled by the processes of the ecosystem if they are used wisely. These are *renewable resources*. Almost all the needs of primitive man were met by renewable resources. With his limited tools and numbers, he seldom damaged the ecosystem. Thus, he seldom had to think about conserving his resources.

Other resources are not replaced, at least not within the span of a few human lifetimes. Coal, petroleum, metal ores, and mineral deposits have been formed over millions of years. New deposits will form eventually, but man is using up these materials so rapidly that they will all be gone within a period of a few centuries at most. It will be a long wait until they are renewed by natural processes. For all practical purposes, these are *nonrenewable resources*.

Today we face serious shortages of both kinds of resources. Careless management in the past and great demands today threaten many of the renewable resources. Our rapid use of the nonrenewable resources makes their exhaustion seem inevitable within the next few generations.

Thus far, man has been ingenious and lucky. He has always been able to find new sources when supplies seemed short. Or he could devise more efficient methods of extracting the nonrenewable resources. Or he could sometimes switch to a new kind of material.

Some hope that we can continue in this fashion. When the metal supplies run out, we might develop plastics to do the same jobs. When the oil and coal are all gone, we may find a way to use solar or nuclear energy. In addition, there is always the hope that new deposits will be found somewhere. Perhaps methods will be developed to process mineral deposits that are not concentrated enough for current mining methods. Others say that sooner or later we will run out of something crucial before we find a substitute.

The problem of the renewable resources never seemed severe until recently. In the past, if the water or soil or wildlife of a region was destroyed, it was always possible to move on to a relatively undamaged place. Within a few human generations, the natural process of succession would usually repair the damage, and the original land could be reoccupied. Of course, a few areas, such as the fertile valleys of the Middle East, were damaged so severely that they became permanent deserts, but there was always good land somewhere else.

Today, however, the entire atmosphere and water supply of the world are being damaged by man. Soils everywhere are being abused. Plants and animals throughout the world are endangered by various changes that man has created. Unless we learn to use these resources wisely, we may unintentionally do permanent damage to the entire ecosystem.

In this chapter, we shall look briefly at some of our natural resources and the problems involved in their conservation and wise use.

The Forests

As we have seen in earlier chapters, a forest is a complex ecosystem that covers the land wherever temperatures and moisture are suitable. The forests of Asia, Europe, and America probably provided the habitat for many of the people of the stone age. Forest plants and animals provide a rich variety of resources for humans living as hunters and gatherers.

However, when man began to raise his own plants and animals, he found it more convenient to clear away the forest. It was easier to produce good farm land by chopping down trees than by struggling against the grasses of the plains. The felled trees provided useful lumber, and after the wild animals were killed, meat could be obtained from cattle and other domestic animals.

In America, the loss of the forests did not seem serious, so long as there were vast forests still standing in the West. Today, as more and more forest land gives way to farms, highways, and suburbs, the shortage of wood is becoming serious. Not only is the price of lumber rising, but wood products such as paper are becoming more expensive as wood becomes scarcer.

Many lumbermen have at last taken note of the situation. Some have begun selectively cutting mature trees from a forest without destroying the entire eco-

Figure 10–2
Clear cutting is different from selective cutting in that patches of a forest are completely lumbered. Because some kinds of trees won't regenerate in shade, clear cutting is a practice recommended over selective cutting in some forests. Both methods of lumbering are an improvment over wholesale destruction of an entire ecosystem.

system. This practice, known as *sustained yield*, leaves most trees uncut at any one time. However, the shortage of wood results in attractively high prices. This has led lumbermen into repeated attempts to obtain rights to cut the remaining natural forests on public lands. The lure of quick profits leads many to destroy forests without the careful management practices just described, whenever it seems possible to get away with it.

Forest survey information suggests that the shortage may not be serious. The United States still has about 759 million acres of forest, of which 500 million acres are commercially usable. Of the usable forest, 140 million acres are owned by federal, state, and local governments.

However, what the statistics do not show is that the great forests that the pioneers found are gone. Except in hard-to-reach mountain regions and in a few preserved areas, all of the big trees are removed. Our modern forests are mostly second growth, composed of young and smaller trees. Every few years, loggers slice through the forests with trucks, bulldozers, and other equipment to remove any trees that have grown to usable size.

The results of these disturbances and of the change in the forest profile are drastic. With the upper canopy removed, more sunlight reaches the forest floor. Grasses and shrubs choke out many of the smaller trees. The animals that lived in the high canopy are gone. New populations have moved in to occupy the thick undergrowth. The entire community has changed. The conditions of the soil have been changed by the new plants and animals. The effects on the trees are not yet known.

Forests also play an important role in regulating the runoff of rainwater. Water is trapped by the plants and the rich soil, seeping only slowly into the streams even after heavy rainstorms. With the forests thinned and the hillsides stripped bare in many places, heavy rainfalls lead to erosion of soil off the hillsides, and flooding in the valleys below.

In the mountains of northwestern California, logging has been extensive in recent years. Much of it has been done with modern methods that are supposed to conserve the forests. In the winter of 1964, a series of heavy rains caused disastrous floods of the rivers of the region. The streams were thick with soil carried down from the logged hillsides. Amidst this scene of destruction, observers in airplanes noted that one stream, Humboldt Creek, was clear and sparkling. Although its waters were deeper than usual, it was not flooding seriously. The entire area drained by Humboldt Creek was owned by a conservation group, and had been preserved in its natural state and protected from logging. The trees were regulating the water runoff and holding the soil on the hillside.

Because of the poor quality of the modern forests, the amount of lumber produced has declined over the past few decades, despite the increasing demand for wood and the improved technology of the loggers. Even with full use of modern methods of forest management, this gap between supply and demand is expected to increase as time goes by.

Foresters are learning about the ecology of forests. They are finding ways to speed up succession to reach the climax population of trees that they wish to harvest. Fertilization of forests, selective cutting, reseeding, controlled use of fire, and the use of chemicals to control pests or unwanted undergrowth are all being applied in attempts to restore or modify the forest ecosystem. Unfortunately, we do not fully understand that ecosystem. We know little, for example, about the cycles of nutrients within the forest or which factors may be crucial to the maintenance of a good soil.

We should keep in mind the fact that man has seldom succeeded in taming the forests. The lands around the Mediterranean Sea were almost entirely stripped of their forests by our ancestors, and the great forests of the Middle East and of northern Africa exist only in ancient stories of once-great civilizations. Within this century, the heavily forested island of Madagascar has been changed to an almost unusable expanse of grasslands. Where man has cut down the forests, the land has often turned to desert. Even the passage of centuries has not produced any sign of succession leading back to similar forests. Clearly, there is an urgent need to learn more about the soil of forests, and the ways that that soil is changed when the trees are removed.

Grasslands and Farmland

When man began to make major changes in the grasslands, his efforts often had catastrophic effects on the ecosystem. The natural grazing animals were eliminated and replaced by cattle. Large herds of cattle, confined by fences, soon overgrazed the prairies. With most of the grass eaten by the cattle, no new litter was added to the mulch layer. Hence that layer soon was decomposed and disappeared. Water was no longer held in the mulch, but flowed away over the land after each rainstorm, washing away much of the soil. Without the protection and nourishment of the mulch, many more plant species were unable to survive. As the land became more and more bare, erosion removed most of the topsoil, leaving sterile dust or sand.

Those farmers who raised grains rather than cattle also had problems. When they destroyed or drove away the predators that ate their chickens and other farm animals, the rodent populations were left unchecked and increased dramatically. Mice, gophers, ground squirrels, and other rodents attacked their grain fields in vast numbers. When a drought arrived, their grains soon died. The soil was no longer protected by the network of grass roots and the layer of mulch. Winds and flash storms carried away much of the topsoil. In the Dust Bowl area of the south central United States, a huge area of rich farmland was destroyed in this fashion during the droughts of the 1930's. One great storm dropped 25 tons of dust per square mile as far away as New England. Robbed of its soil, this area became a virtual desert. Even 40 years later, it has not recovered.

Figure 10–3

In flat, treeless prairie, overgrazed soil unprotected by roots and mulch is readily carried away by wind during a dry period.

When crops are harvested, most of the plant material is removed from the land. The nutrients are not returned to the soil as they would be in a natural ecosystem. To replace the nutrients, the farmer adds various chemical fertilizers. These fertilizers are designed to replace the ingredients known to be needed in the soil. Unfortunately, the chemicals are often added in proportions or compounds that make the soil unsuitable for the decomposers and other organisms that live there. In the presence of excess nitrogen fertilizers, the nitrogen-fixing bacteria die out. More and more of the natural cycles cease to function. The farmer is forced to supply all the needs of his crops. Many biologists warn that ever-increasing dosages of fertilizers and pesticides will be needed to maintain high production rates, and that eventually even these will not be enough.

Optimistic farm experts hope that a careful application of the principles of ecology to farming will prevent future disasters. Pesticides and fertilizers can be used cautiously, with careful attention to the condition of the soil community. Insects can be controlled by other methods, such as interplanting of varied crops or use of natural enemies of the pest insects. Rotation of crops or occasional planting of legumes (such as clover) to be plowed under can help replenish the soil.

As we shall see in the next chapter, the production of ever greater amounts of food will be necessary in the coming decades. Here, as in almost every area of consideration in this chapter, there is currently a debate between the optimists and the pessimists. The optimists—mostly agricultural scientists and technologists—expect to bring ever more land under cultivation through irrigation and to vastly increase the yield of the existing land through fertilization, pest control, and improved kinds of crop plants. The pessimists—mostly conservationists and ecologists—see many potential problems, and warn that only intensive study and application of ecological principles can avoid future disasters.

Land Use

With our increasing population, land itself has become an important natural resource. It is no longer possible to find unlimited open space a few miles down the road when things get crowded.

In 1800, if the land of the United States could have been divided up equally, each person would have had 104 acres. By 1900 there were only 25 acres for each person. In the mid 1960's, each person could claim only about 11 acres. By 1975 the figure will be under 10 acres.

That seems like a lot of space. Why is there any

problem? Isn't 10 acres ample space for one person? In the first place, that figure includes your share of all the unusable desert, swamp, and mountain land. It also includes between two and three acres of cropland that produce the food you eat. It includes your share of the highways, industries, commercial buildings, parking lots, schools, parks, government installations, and other human constructions that already occupy most of the usable land.

The demand for land today is tremendous. New suburbs and highways are being built each day. Agricultural land and parks near cities are rapidly being lost to the expanding urban areas. Careful and intelligent planning for the use of land in a large region occurs only in a few places. More and more such planning will be needed as our population grows.

Many conservationists are now becoming concerned about the need to preserve areas of open space and wilderness. They argue that these are not simply luxuries.

Figure 10–4

The Los Angeles freeway system is an example of the way we have chosen to use our land, in this case giving the automobile precedence over everything else in the community.

As people are crowded into cities, with less chance to wander in open spaces or among trees and flowers and animals, they may feel a pressing need for escape. Earlier in this book we mentioned certain experiments in which overcrowding and unnatural surroundings produce peculiar behavior. The animals seem to become very anxious and disturbed. They may fight one another, kill their own offspring, or simply become sickly and die. Some psychologists see parallels between these experiments and the increasing crime rate, suicide rate, and other problems in our cities. In any case, it seems clear that people will be better able to stand the crowded conditions of the city if they can escape occasionally to the quiet of a park or forest.

Ecologists suggest another reason for preserving wilderness areas. If we build cities and farms on all the available land, we will eventually have imposed our simplified artificial ecosystem on most of the land surface of the earth. Most species of plants and animals that occupy the various habitats of the land would become extinct. This oversimplified ecosystem—extending over an entire continent or the entire world—would be most vulnerable to population crashes. A change in climate or a pollution problem might destroy the plant populations of the human-built ecosystem. It would then be vital to have preserved isolated examples of various ecosystems, from which populations could come to replace the lost populations of the simplified ecosystem. Even if there were no such disaster, we might discover some day that one of the organisms we had eliminated played a vital role in some cycle of the world ecosystem. Again, preservation of wilderness areas would make it likely that a small population of that organism would still survive. Finally, there is great value in keeping samples of those ecosystems around for study, so that we can learn more about the ways in which different ecosystems operate.

Other Resources

Space does not permit complete discussions of other natural resources. We can only mention here a few of the most important, with brief comments.

The early conservationists were greatly concerned about the preservation of wildlife. Much of the interest in wildlife conservation is among those who enjoy hunting and fishing as sports. Wildlife management is now a major field of study and employment, and many of our advances in ecological understanding have come from the work of those in this field. When they attempted to maintain a population of game birds, for example, they soon learned that it was necessary to pay attention to the entire eco-system. To keep the birds alive, it was necessary to main-tain the right kinds of plant cover and food, proper soil and water conditions, and even a complex community of other organisms that played a role in the ecosystem. As in the case of the Kaibab deer, they learned that even the well-meaning destruction of predators might have a harmful effect. Today most species in danger of extinction are protected from hunting, and even given every assis-tance toward survival in game reserves.

However, many species are on the verge of extinc-tion, not because of direct killing by man, but because vital elements of their environment have been altered by man. Some believe that the passenger pigeon would have become extinct even had man not hunted it so inten-sively. The passenger pigeon needed the vast forests of the eastern United States, and these were removed. The caribou and the wolverine are in danger of extinction today, for they can survive only in large wilderness areas. Arguments given for preservation of wildlife go far beyond the simple pleasure of keeping alive a few ani-mals for hunting or watching. There is also a question of man's moral right to destroy other creatures that have inhabited the earth for at least as long as he has.

Pollution

Much attention is being given today to the resources of air and water. These resources once seemed inexhausti-ble. Today the supplies of fresh air and water seem in definite danger of running out. The problem is chiefly one of pollution. The air and water are not disappearing, but they can be made unusable, because they are carrying a cargo of harmful substances. Like every other animal, man contributes waste products to the environment. Under normal conditions, human wastes are eventually returned to the nutrient supply by the decomposers. However, the huge number of humans in the world today makes the sheer volume of waste that we produce a strain upon the decomposing ability of the system. Even more important, the waste products tend to be concentrated in particular places, such as in the outflow of city sewage systems. Much of the pollution comes not from human waste, but from industrial plants and machines such as the automobile.

Figure 10–5

Ducks paddle away as 8000 gallons of sludge from a nearby paper mill are dumped into a pond from a converted oil truck.

Many of the chemicals produced and dumped into the ecosystem are of types not normally present in the environment. Some cannot be broken down by the decomposers. We have already discussed problems of pesticide pollution in the oceans. Other problems are more subtle. Many industrial plants use water for cooling, and then dump the heated water back into streams or the oceans. Although this water may not be polluted by poisons, it is polluted by excess heat. Its temperature may be high enough to destroy it as an environment for living organisms. Burning of coal and petroleum products has significantly increased the concentration of carbon dioxide in the atmosphere. This may lead to serious changes in the climate of the earth. Pollution of the atmosphere or oceans with radioactive materials produced by man poses a serious threat to all life on earth. The problems of pollution are extremely serious ones, and vast amounts of money and of research will be needed if our children are not to live in sealed compartments, breathing filtered air and venturing outside only with gas masks.

Applied Ecology

Until a few decades ago, the problems of conservation seemed relatively unimportant and isolated. Some wanted to save birds and animals, others hoped to give their grandchildren a chance to walk in a forest, still others worried about the redwood trees or the supply of good hunting grounds. Most people saw these as good ideas, but as luxuries to be obtained whenever they did not interfere too much with the activities of man.

Today, more and more people are coming to realize that conservation of the environment is a single problem that is vital to the survival of the human species—perhaps to the survival of life on earth. All of the problems discussed in this chapter can be solved only through a better understanding of the total ecosystem—the ecosphere called Spaceship Earth.

Test Yourself

1. Conservation of natural resources used to be the concern of rather few people: those who saw that we might run out of some resources and those who cared about natural scenery and wildlife. Suddenly, in our time, millions of people are becoming interested in conservation. Why?

2. What are the differences between renewable and nonrenewable resources? Give examples.

3. What other uses does a forest have besides growing wood, feeding animals, and providing scenery and recreation for people?

4. What is the Dust Bowl area of the United States, and why does it have this name? What happened there?

5. For what practical reasons do ecologists say that some wild ecosystems should be preserved in their wild state?

6. Comment upon the implications of the following definitions of conservation. Which seems best to you? Why?

    (a) Conservation is the attempt to ration our use of natural resources so that some will be left for the future.

    (b) Conservation is the attempt, through careful management and planning, to avoid injury to the environment.

    (c) Conservation is applied ecology.

    (d) Conservation is the attempt to balance our use of natural resources and our replenishment of the environment, to insure a steady supply of necessary materials.

7. Is there a distinction between *conservation* and *ecology*? If so, what?

8. Francis Bacon once wrote: "We cannot command nature except by obeying her." What does this statement mean? How does it apply to the problems discussed in this chapter?

9. In the mid-1960's, the United States, with less than 7 percent of the world's population, was consuming about 60 percent of the mineral resources currently being taken from the earth. What implications does this have about pollution problems, conservation of resources, or the future of the under-developed nations?

10. The pollution problems in and around our modern cities seem to be much more severe than those of large, densely populated cities of past ages. Why?

Human Population

Population Crisis

There has been a great deal of talk in recent years about the "population explosion." It is said that the human population is increasing so rapidly that widespread famine is inevitable in the near future. There is a great deal of debate about the methods that should be used to slow down or stop the growth of the human population.

This is a very controversial topic. People have strong feelings about the right to have children, or the need to limit population growth. Many feel that any interference with the natural birth rate is immoral. Others see the population-control movement as an attempt of rich white people to keep what they have and hold down the rest of the world in the process. On the other side, some maintain that continued high birth rates are immoral, for they will lead to misery and starvation for millions.

There are no simple answers to the problems of human population. In this chapter we simply look at some of the available information about what has happened to the human population in the past. We try to apply some of the principles of ecology to explain the changes in population and talk about the possibilities for the future. You will have to make up your own mind about the course of action that seems best for you.

The Human Population
Over the Centuries

Like all population statistics, those on the human species involve many estimates and assumptions. Census figures provide fairly reliable information on populations in the industrial nations over the past several decades. However, information for other countries and for the more distant past is based upon estimates, and these are often indirect. Although the figures are not exact, there can be no doubt that the human population has increased drastically over the centuries.

The earliest men are thought to have been hunters and food-gatherers. Living as an omnivore, fairly high in the food web, man could not have had a very dense population. From studies of the few cultures that still live in this fashion, we can estimate the amount of land that early man could have occupied, and his maximum population density on that land. Such methods lead to an estimate that the human population probably reached a maximum of about 5 million persons by the time agriculture was invented.

The fossil evidence suggests that man spread over the earth rather slowly, and that it took a very long time to reach this number. For the first few million years of his existence, man probably lived only in Africa. The total population there probably was never much more than 100,000. By about 6000 B.C., man occupied much of the world, and the population was near the 5-million limit for a hunting and gathering society.

At about this time, man learned to domesticate plants and animals. With the increased food supply from farming, a higher population density could be supported on

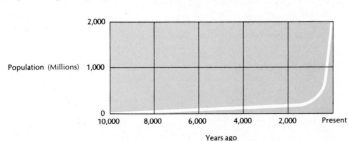

Figure 11–1

The growth of human population, shown as an arithmetic curve, from 10,000 years ago to the present.

the land. The population increased. By the time of Christ, the human population probably numbered 130 million. It reached 500 million about 1650 A.D.

Although these figures are largely guesswork, the numbers from this time on are thought to be fairly reliable. The population doubled in size in about 200 years, reaching 1 billion about 1850. The next doubling, to 2 billion, took only about 80 years, for that population was reached about 1930. At this writing, the next doubling had not quite been completed. The population reached 3.5 billion sometime in 1968. At the current rate of growth, the time required for doubling of the population is less than 40 years. Keep this in mind: the time required for doubling the population keeps getting shorter.

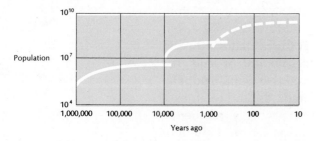

Figure 11–2

Plotting population growth logarithmically (using powers of ten) makes it possible to show trends over a longer period in a small space. Three surges become evident: one reflecting the beginnings of toolmaking, one after the development of agriculture, and one following the industrial revolution.

Let's review what has happened. It took more than 2 million years for mankind to reach a population of half a billion. It took only 200 years to double that and reach the first billion. The next doubling required 80 years, and was complete by 1930, when the earth had 2 billion people. Now the earth has more than 3.5 billion people. It is expected to have 7 billion people by the year 2000, another doubling in only three decades.

It is clear that the rate of growth itself is increasing. This is shown in the following table, which gives the annual increase in population expressed as a percentage of the total population at the time. The figures have been averaged over several years to show the general trend.

Period	Annual population growth rate
1750–1800	0.3 %
1800–1850	0.4 %
1850–1900	0.5 %
1900–1950	1.0 %
1950–1960	1.9 %
1960–1970	2.0 % +

The Present Human Population

At the beginning of the 1970's, the human population was about 3.6 billion, and increasing at a rate of more than 2 percent per year. This means that *every day*, about 200,000 more people were being added to the human population.

The picture is not a simple one, however. The human population is not evenly distributed over the earth. Where the climate and abundant resources make a higher population density possible, the greatest numbers of people are gathered. Other parts of the earth are almost uninhabited.

Table 11-1 gives some idea of the variety of conditions around the world. Population figures are estimates for mid-1971. The growth rates are derived from the latest available published estimates of the United Nations.

As you can see from the table, the rates of population growth are lowest in the industrialized countries, and highest in the so-called underdeveloped countries. The reasons for this are debatable and will be discussed in a later section. You may recall from Chapter 5 that the population growth rate is related to the annual excess of births over deaths. To show this relationship, the estimated crude birth and death rates for 1971 have been added to the table. These represent the number of births and deaths for each 1000 persons in the population. The difference between birth and death rates does not correspond exactly to the growth rate shown because of migration and other factors.

In most of the world, there are about 7 to 20 deaths per 1000 population per year. In the countries with the lower population growth rates, there are about 18 to 20 births per 1000 population per year. In the countries with high growth rates, there are about 35 to 50 births per 1000 population per year.

Why do the underdeveloped countries seem to have such high birth rates? In fact, a study of the historical figures shows that the birth rates in those countries are normal. It is the low birth rates of the developed countries that are unusual.

Table 11-1   1971 Population Statistics for Various Countries

Country	Population (millions)	Population density*	Annual population growth	Crude birth rate	Crude death rate
United Kingdom	56	228	0.5%	17	12
France	51.5	93	0.7%	17	11
Italy	54.1	178	0.8%	18	10
Poland	33.3	105	0.9%	16	8
Spain	33.6	66	1.0%	20	9
U.S.S.R.	245	11	1.0%	17	8
Japan	104.7	280	1.1%	18	7
United States	207.1	22	1.1%	18	9
Argentina	24.7	9	1.5%	22	9
Canada	21.8	2	1.7%	18	7
China (mainland)	772.9	79	1.8%	33	15
Ethiopia	25.6	20	2.1%	46	25
Burma	28.4	41	2.3%	40	17
China (Taiwan)	14.3	390	2.3%	26	5
South Korea	32.9	323	2.5%	36	11
India	569.5	168	2.6%	42	17
Nigeria	56.5	60	2.6%	50	25
Turkey	36.5	45	2.7%	43	16
United Arab Republic	8.0	33	2.8%	50	23
Indonesia	124.9	81	2.9%	47	19
Brazil	95.7	11	3.0%	38	10
Iran	29.2	17	3.0%	48	18
Pakistan	141.6	121	3.3%	50	18
Thailand	37.4	70	3.3%	42	10
Colómbia	22.1	19	3.4%	44	11
Mexico	52.4	26	3.4%	42	9
Philippines	39.4	128	3.4%	46	12

Figures were furnished by Population Reference Bureau, Inc.
*Population density is given in persons per square kilometer. The figures are for 1970.

Birth and Death Rates in the Past

We know little about the birth and death rates of ancient man. However, from the skeletons that have been found, we can make a good guess that, if Neanderthal man survived beyond infancy, he lived on the average about 29 or 30 years. Remains and records of children who died during the first year of life are very scarce for these distant times. But it seems reasonable to think that there was a high infant death rate, since low infant death rates have only been achieved in this century.

The average life span is calculated by including all members of a population that die, regardless of age. Thus, to use an exaggerated hypothetical example, if half the population dies in infancy and the other half lives to the age of 50, the average life span is 25. So, although many Neanderthals may have lived to be 30, the *average* life span may have been somewhere between 20 and 30, taking into account infant mortality and other deaths in between. Even at the height of ancient Greek and Roman civilizations, the average life span was probably about 35 years, and it remained much the same throughout the Middle Ages and on into the nineteenth century.

If only about half of the children born in a population live to become parents themselves, each couple has to produce at least four children just to keep the population constant. The fact that the population has steadily grown suggests that the average family over the centuries has probably been larger than that.

In many modern cultures young people begin to have children as soon as they are able. Where there are no cultural influences to limit the number of births, the crude birth rate is about 40 to 50 births per thousand population per year. It seems reasonable to suppose that this has been the typical birth rate for the human race throughout much of its existence.

With the beginning of the industrial age, death rates began to decrease steadily. There were a number of reasons for this. Better means of transportation made it possible to bring food from distant areas when famine threatened. New techniques of farming produced better supplies of food from the old farms, and new sources of power permitted irrigation of land that had been too dry for agriculture. As medical knowledge increased and public health practices were improved, the death rate dropped even more rapidly.

The diseases that had formerly killed many children before they grew up were the first to be controlled. Thus the population began to shift toward a higher percentage of young people, and thus of people likely to produce children. Over the century between 1750 and 1850, the death rate in England and Wales declined from 32 to 22

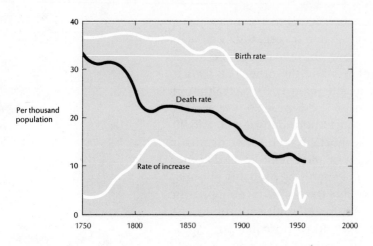

40

30

Per thousand
population   20

10

0

1750   1800   1850   1900   1950   2000

Birth rate

Death rate

Rate of increase

Figure 11–3

Vital statistics for England and Wales between 1750 and 1950. What are thought to be some reasons for the marked decrease in birth rate that occurred after 1850 in these and other industrialized countries?

per thousand, while the birth rate remained nearly constant at about 37 per thousand (see Figure 11-3). As a result, the growth rate of the population increased from about 0.3 percent to about 1.6 percent per year.

As the population increased rapidly, two things happened. First, a large number of persons left Europe, most of them moving to the United States, Canada, Australia, and South Africa. Second, the birth rate began to drop, causing the population growth rate to decline again.

There is a great deal of debate about the reason for this drop in the birth rate. Probably it was caused by a combination of factors. It appears that there was no great effect of starvation or physical overcrowding. Instead, many people simply married later and had fewer children. The emigrants tended to be young, leaving an older average population in the home countries.

On the farms, a large family had often been an advantage. The children helped to work the land. When they grew up, they built new farms nearby and helped out their parents. As the industries arose in the cities, more and more young people left to seek the new jobs there. Meanwhile, fertile land became more scarce. A large family now was little or no advantage to the farmer. In the city, things were even worse. Even with child labor, a parent had to support each child for several years before he could begin to work and pay for his own keep. If a parent wished his child to advance in the world, he had to pay for an expensive education and support him for many more years. A working man with a large family could only expect to barely keep them all fed and clothed, and to see them continue in poverty throughout their lives. Furthermore, the decrease in infant death rates meant that it was no longer necessary to have four children in order to see two grow up. With increasing life spans, the father might have to support his own aged parents as well as his children.

For all of these and probably many other reasons, people in England began to have fewer children. During the century from 1850 to 1950, the birth rate dropped rapidly. Even though the death rate also continued to decrease, the population growth rate again dropped to less than 1 percent per year.

This same pattern has been observed in almost every country that has been industrialized during the past century. By the middle of the twentieth century, it appeared that population growth rates in Europe, North America, and Japan had nearly leveled off at low rates. These rates are about 1 percent per year. This is similar to the rates of growth existing before the death rate was lowered.

In the rest of the world, however, the situation is quite different. During the first half of this century, medical advances were applied throughout the world. Techniques of irrigation, fertilization, and insect control have been spread to every country, greatly reducing the chances of true starvation. The combination of improved food supply and medical care has caused a drastic drop in the death rate, particularly among infants, throughout the world. In some tropical countries, for example, the use of DDT to control insects that carry diseases to humans has by itself nearly cut the death rate in half.

As we saw in Table 11-1, the death rates in these countries are now nearly as low as those in the industrialized nations. The birth rate, however, has remained nearly unchanged. As a result, the growth rate of these populations is very high. The poorest countries—those where food is already in short supply, and starvation and misery are common—are increasing in population most rapidly. The industrialized countries—where there is ample food and space—are growing in population relatively slowly.

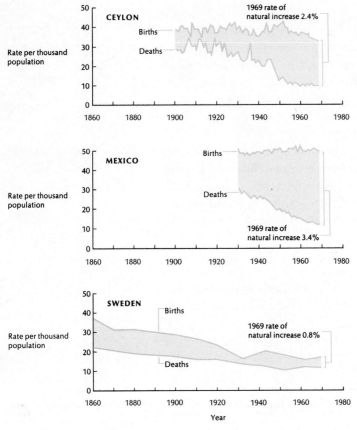

Figure 11–4

While the death rate has dropped markedly all over the world in the last century, the birth rate has remained relatively stable in nonindustrialized countries. How does this affect population growth in these countries?

What has created this odd situation, and what should be done about it? At first glance, it might seem that there is no great problem. It took nearly a century for the birth rate to begin to drop after the drop in death rate in the industrialized nations. We might expect the same thing to happen in the rest of the world. According to this theory, the high growth rates are temporary; they will soon vanish as these countries become industrialized.

Demographers (students of population) are becoming less hopeful about this possibility, however. They point out that conditions are different in these countries in several ways.

First, the rate of population growth is much higher than it ever was in the industrial nations. In Europe and Japan, the growth rate never rose much above 1.5 percent per year. In the United States, the growth rate may have been as high as 3 percent around 1800. However, this was largely due to the large numbers of younger people coming in from Europe. These caused an increase in the birth rate that was not matched by deaths among older people. Such an imbalance is temporary, and by 1850 the U.S. growth rate had dropped below 1.5 percent. Furthermore, the United States had vast amounts of land available for a rapidly growing population. In the underdeveloped nations of today, the high growth rates are not due to temporary imbalances caused by immigration, and there is no vacant land available.

A growth rate of 3 percent leads to a doubling of the population every 23 years. This means that merely to maintain their present standard of living, these nations will have to double their food production, their supply of housing, their roads and factories, and everything else in two decades.

The situation is made worse by the fact that the sudden population growth has come at a much earlier stage of development than it did in Europe, America, or Japan. When the European countries reached their highest population growth, nearly half of their people lived in cities and nearly a third of them worked in factories. The shift to full industrialization was well underway, and it was much easier to increase industrial production to provide for the growing population. Furthermore, the pressures that we have noted to decrease the birth rate seemed to work most effectively in the cities.

In the underdeveloped nations of today, more than two-thirds of the people live outside of cities, and only about 15 percent work in factories. A tremendous change in the society would be needed to reach full industrialization. Such a change seems almost impossible when every effort is being turned to the attempt to feed and house the rapidly growing population.

Peter Drucker, an economist and business expert, recently pointed out that no nation has become industrialized since World War I. He argues that such industrialization is no longer possible in the old ways, for reasons that include some of those we have discussed. He feels that concentrated assistance from the industrialized nations might possibly help nonindustrialized countries attain developed status. However, far more than our present foreign aid would be needed. Paul Ehrlich, the ecologist, is more pessimistic. He refers to these as the "never-to-be-developed" countries.

It appears, then, that we cannot relax in the hope that these nations will soon have lower population growth rates as they become industrialized. However, it is possible that the birth rate will drop for other reasons. The population density in many of these countries is far greater than that of pre-industrial Europe. Famine is an ever-present threat. Modern communications bring them news of the rich life in the low-birth-rate and industrialized countries, and also bring information on ways to limit the size of families. As a result of these factors, birth rates might begin to decline without industrialization. The governments of many countries, such as China and India, have made strong efforts to encourage small families.

Meanwhile, there are signs that birth rates may drop still lower in the industrialized nations. Although food shortages seem remote in these nations, the steadily increasing populations have created new problems. As we saw in earlier chapters, the shortage of clean air and water, open space, and natural beauty may become severe enough to cause people to want to reduce the size of their families.

Future Population Trends— Starvation?

It is clear that the present rate of growth of the human population cannot continue for very long. At present, the world population is doubling about every 35 years, and the doubling time is decreasing rapidly. Even if the doubling continued to take 35 years, it would take less than 400 years to fill the entire land area of the earth to the density of New York's Manhattan Island. In about 850 years, the population would reach about 60,000,000,000,-000,000, or about 100 persons for each square yard of surface (including both land and sea).

There seems to be no doubt that the human population will have to level off long before that point. There would be no room for the people to stand, much less for crops to be grown. Incidentally, space travel offers no solution. It has been calculated that it would take less than two centuries to fill every planet in the solar system to the same human density as the earth. When you recall that the human population is currently increasing by about 200,000 persons *per day*, you realize that even a vast effort by the industrial nations could not hope to stop population growth by shipping the excess people off into space.

Besides, the other planets in our solar system are not suitable environments for man. They lack air and liquid water. Some are too hot and some too cold. We would have to make them over, somehow, to make them hospitable to man. But our pressing problem right now is to see whether we can keep our own earth suitable for man.

Even if the birth rate were drastically lowered immediately, population would probably continue to grow for some time. This is because most of the underdeveloped countries have nearly half of their populations below the age of child-bearing. Even if each couple limited itself to two children, the growth rate would remain high for a long time. After all, many couples would be producing their two children long before they themselves or their own parents died.

As we have seen, population growth cannot possibly continue at its present high rate for more than a few centuries. The growth rate can only be decreased by changes in the birth or death rate, or both. What might cause these changes? The three major causes of increases in the death rate during man's history have been starvation, war, and disease. There seems to be very strong possibilities that these factors will greatly increase the human death rate in the future.

In the past few centuries, starvation has seldom been a major cause of death in the Western world. But more than three quarters of the people living in the underdeveloped nations get by on inadequate diets. They receive enough food to stay alive, but are severely weak-

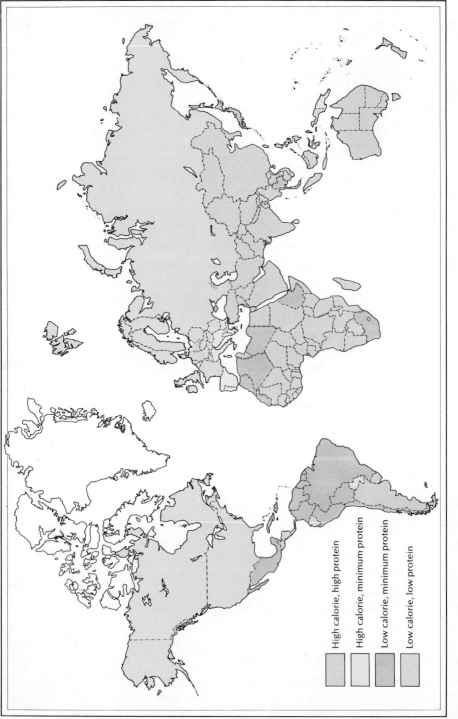

High calorie, high protein

High calorie, minimum protein

Low calorie, minimum protein

Low calorie, low protein

Figure 11–5 Patterns of diet throughout the world. Approximately what percentage of the world's population lives on a low calorie, low protein diet?

ened. They are then apt to die as a result of some disease that would not kill a well-fed person. Thus many deaths caused by food shortages are not actually due to starvation, but to disease. Starvation normally becomes a cause of death only under certain conditions. When a population depends upon crops for its food, and a normal year's crop is just large enough to barely feed the population, the stage is set for a famine. In a normal year, many people are receiving inadequate diets. A drought, a flood, or an unusually hot or cold year may significantly reduce the year's harvest. Then large numbers of people may starve. In Asia, throughout much of recorded history, each year has brought famines in some parts of the continent.

Will starvation be a major factor in the future? Opinions differ. Many optimistic predictions are made about bringing new land into production, increasing the yield on the land now being farmed, or finding new food sources in the sea or through synthetic processes. Other students of the problem are convinced that these advances cannot possibly keep pace with the vast increase in population.

About 80 percent of the increased food production in hungry nations since World War II has been achieved through putting new land into use. Much of this land has been of poor quality for farming. It may have poor soil, water shortages, steep inclines, hot or cold temperatures, and invasions of native plants and insect pests. These force the farmer to struggle continually to obtain some sparse crops from his lands. Pesticides and fertilizers, improved breeds of crop plants, and irrigation projects may help to solve some of these problems in some places. However, such projects are expensive and time consuming.

Dramatic increases in crop yield have come, recently, through the use of hybrid strains of crop plants. What is often overlooked is that the farmer must purchase new seeds each year, since the hybrids themselves do not produce usable seeds for the next year's crop. The farmer who uses fertilizers and pesticides is also forced to spend much of his income to purchase these materials. In most cases, the profits from sales of these materials go to companies in the industrialized world. Thus wealth is continually removed from the hungry nations and concentrated even more heavily in the industrialized nations.

Before World War II, many of the underdeveloped countries were exporters of grains. In recent decades, they have been importing grain to meet the needs of their rapidly increasing populations. At the present time, the world's food supply is slightly less than adequate to feed the population. As the population continues to grow, famines are likely to become more common. Many ecologists and others expect severe famines in Asia, Africa, and possibly in South America during the 1970's. These may be so severe as to significantly lower or even reverse the growth of the human population, at least temporarily.

Eventually, it may be possible to supply food for a much larger population than we now have. If all the usable land area of the world were farmed at maximum efficiency, and all losses to insects and plant diseases could be stopped, we could probably support a population of 8 or even 10 billion people. With efficient use of the oceans and synthetic foods, even larger populations might be supported. Some scientists estimate that as technology develops and new ways of making synthetic food are invented, a few hundred billion people could be supported if food were all they needed.

However, such projections seem meaningless at the present. It has not been possible to distribute our existing food to the starving peoples of the world. The wealth needed for the great projects for making major increases in food production is simply not available to the parts of the world that need it. Many scientists now feel that it is too late to do anything to prevent the death of a sizeable proportion of the human population in the famines of the next decades.

War and Disease

As we have seen, starvation alone is often not the major limitation on human population. Everyone is aware of the dangers of war in the modern world, and of wars of a scale that could destroy much of the human race. Needless to say, the tensions created when more than half of the world is starving, while a minority live in luxury, do not decrease the chances for wars. If serious famines do occur, violence of some sort is almost certain to accompany them.

Diseases also pose a great threat to the undernourished billions of the present population. Modern medicine has greatly controlled the fatal epidemics that once swept great parts of the human population. No plague of any serious disease has struck Europe since 1800. Unfortunately, medical scientists are not certain why this is so. They do not know of any techniques introduced during the 1800's that should have prevented plagues. Because they do not know exactly why the plagues stopped, they are not certain whether they could reappear in the future.

Recently, there have been rapid outbreaks of influenza across the entire world. Infectious diseases can move with great speed in this age of airplane travel. Doctors have been able to treat the victims of these influenza epidemics, preventing most deaths. But they have not succeeded in stopping the spread of the disease. Some fear that an outbreak of a fatal disease might be equally unstoppable if it once got started, and that it might be of such a form that treatment of the victims could not prevent great numbers of deaths.

However, for the moment, it appears that disease may be one of the least likely causes of an increase in the death rate for the human population. Only when the population is weakened and disrupted by famine will it be likely that diseases will take a great toll. It appears that famine or war are most likely to interrupt the upward sweep of the human population curve.

Future Trends in Birth Rates

If the human birth rate could be reduced to a level nearly equal to the death rate, the population curve would also level off. If the peoples of the world could all be persuaded to limit themselves to small families, the population growth rate could be reduced to nearly zero. The population might then be maintained at a level that could be supported on the earth. Unfortunately, there seems to be little evidence that such a change in attitudes will occur within the next decade. Even if it occurred immediately, it might be too late to prevent the famines or wars that seem likely. There are such large numbers of young people in the world population today that the crude birth rate would remain high for many years, even if the individuals chose to produce fewer offspring.

Some ecologists have pointed out that many mechanisms operate in natural ecosystems to decrease the birth rate before actual starvation begins. Some animals have territorial behaviors that limit the breeding population. Others show signs of psychological or physical stress when overcrowded, resulting in lowered birth rates.

Thus far, there is little evidence to show that man's birth rate will be limited in this fashion. There seems to be little relationship between the degree of overcrowding and the human birth rate. Birth rates do drop when people are starving in a famine. They also drop during a war, largely because most of the men are separated from their families. However, there is little indication that human birth rates drop when food supplies are scarce or when a war seems imminent. In fact, there is some evidence which tends to suggest that birth rates become higher in such situations.

In fact, from the history of the human population one is forced to conclude that only cultural changes or actual catastrophes will cause the birth rate to decrease. Since cultural changes normally occur very slowly, many ecologists have concluded that famine, war, and disease will be the factors most likely to bring about the inevitable decline in the population growth rate.

What Can Be Done?

Even in this long chapter, we have been able to touch on only a few of the issues involved in the population problem. Of course, the question of rising population is closely related to the problems of conservation of resources discussed in the last chapter. In discussing population problems, most people miss the point that the per person demand for most resources keeps going up. You use more in the way of resources than your parents did at your age and far more than your grandparents. For example, more water is used in growing crops to feed you, in making steel for the car you ride in, or in making plastics or metals for your sporting goods than was used for any one person 25 years ago. This is because you live in a highly industrialized country. The per capita consumption of resources in underdeveloped countries is nowhere near as high as in ours. In fact, it has been estimated that the average American consumes 20 times the resources of a person living in India. Thus, although the U.S. population growth rate is relatively slow, our consumption of resources severely taxes the whole planet, damaging the chances for a decent life for future human beings.

Test Yourself

1. About when did the earth's human population reach 1 billion? How long did it take for the population to reach 2 billion? What is the human population now? By when is it expected to have doubled again?
2. Have birth rates or death rates been more important in achieving the rapid growth of human population in our century?
3. Why would the population in a typical underdeveloped country continue to increase even if the birth rate were soon lowered to equal the death rate?
4. Why does it seem unlikely that underdeveloped countries will cut their birth rates automatically once they become industrialized?
5. What were the three main checks on human population in the past? Which ones are expected to be most serious in the next few decades?

6. Is food supply the only thing that humanity has to worry about as its population explodes? That is, if we can just solve the food problem, does it look as if we can accept unlimited population growth? What else would you say is involved?

7. It is suggested that the earth could support many more billions of people if food production were limited to a few simple crops, such as wheat and rice, and all people became primary consumers. Discuss this proposal in the light of what you have read in this book, and of what you can find out about the history of Ireland in the 1840's.

8. Less than 10 percent of the land area of the earth is currently farmed. Why should it not be possible to increase the food supply at least five or six times by expanding into the unfarmed lands?

9. One ecologist recently stated that the population problem is the most important one facing man today. "If we solve this problem, we will have a chance at solving all of the others. If we don't solve the population problem, none of the others will matter." Discuss this statement in view of the information in this chapter. Aren't such problems as racial tensions and prevention of nuclear war more urgent than population limitation?

The Ecology
of the City

The City as a Habitat

A city is a habitat for man. It is not a natural habitat, of course; it is one that man has invented. Nowadays a majority of the people of the United States live in cities or in urban areas around and between cities. Seven out of ten Americans can now be considered city people, and this is bcoming a pattern for the whole world.

For a long time, perhaps thousands of years, people have thought of the city as something distinct from the country, meaning the rest of the land. Thus, out of habit, people have thought of the city as apart from nature and independent of it. Leaders, experts, and ordinary citizens have tried to solve the problems of the city as if these ideas were true. Of course they are not true. The city is part of the local environment. It is a habitat in which man can live, but it is not an ecosystem in itself. In this book we have seen that an ecosystem is fairly independent, with production and consumption of food and recycling of materials going on within it. But a city depends on the surrounding world for all the needs of life.

In this chapter, we are attempting something almost entirely new. We are taking an ecological view of the city. Studies of city problems that were called ecological were made more than 40 years ago, but the ecology concerned the relationships between industries, businesses, building patterns, transportation systems, and groupings of people. Little that was truly ecological was considered. The term had been borrowed from biology and was artificially applied. This seemed proper at the time, since the city itself is artificial. Even so, a city has relationships to the natural environment and to living organisms. Like anything else, it both acts upon and is affected by its environment.

The Original Cities

To gain perspective on the modern city and its ecology, it is helpful to think about how cities developed. The earliest known cities came into existence about 5,500 years ago. Their ruins have been discovered in the part of Asia long known as the Fertile Crescent, though much of it is desert today. Various fabled empires, such as Babylon, once flourished there.

The first fact to keep in mind about the earliest cities is that they were all surrounded by the best farmland of their particular region. This was no accident. It was true for most cities right down to modern times. Nor was it an accident that the earliest cities, and most of the important cities built since, were built on the banks of sizeable rivers. The rivers gave an abundant and dependable supply of water and were used for disposal of sewage and wastes. They were highways for trade and for bringing in many of the things the cities needed from the surrounding region, food as well as building materials and metals. During the industrial revolution of the seventeenth, eighteenth, and nineteenth centuries, new cities also needed rivers for water power. Rivers still have these uses today.

Although some early cities may have grown from older villages, most early cities seem to have been planned right from the start. Their sizes seem to have been decided upon in advance, and each had a definite shape. There was a place for a temple, a place for granaries, and a marketplace for farm produce. There was a residence and offices for the rulers, one or more zones for tradesmen's workshops, and housing for the citizens. Major buildings were arranged around a large open space or square.

Figure 12–1

Ephesus, in western Turkey, was founded about 1300 B.C. by the Greeks, and later inhabited by the early Christians and the Romans. It is now being gradually excavated and restored as an archeological masterpiece. Like most ancient cities, it was a carefully planned complex of apartments and houses, government buildings, a place of worship, an outdoor theater, and a marketplace. The photos show the remains of the outdoor theater and the marble-paved, statue-lined avenue that led to the sea.

Early cities were quite compact, and so were most newer cities through thousands of years. For most people, walking was the only way to get around. It was intended that anybody could reach any part of the city from any other part in a fairly short walk. This would be essential, of course, if the city were attacked—there were no helicopters to speed defenders to trouble spots. But the compactness had other advantages. It made everything the city had to offer, all its variety, its entertainment and shopping and schooling as well as work, easy to find and reach.

Rome, about two thousand years ago, had gradually gained a population of more than a million people. The Roman rulers found themselves issuing traffic regulations for chariots and wagons. Rome began to solve its problem of urban sprawl by founding new towns, not only near itself but in other parts of the Roman Empire. This protected Rome and other important cities from excessive growth, and from being choked by their rings of suburbs.

Wheels and Growth

Until about a century ago, the most common mode of transportation was still walking. For business to proceed at any kind of a rapid pace, a city could not expand beyond the distances a messenger could walk in an hour or two. Given an average walking speed of 3 miles an hour, a city might be 6 miles in diameter at most.

Then, about a century ago, the street railway became common. The electric trolley car and then the motor bus and the subway abolished the walking-distance limit. The invention of the telephone directly stimulated growth, since information could be exchanged without the constant travel of messengers. Another invention, the powered elevator, made taller buildings practical. This made it possible to have higher population densities in cities than before.

About 70 years ago, the automobile and the motor truck came into use. These removed limits as to where factories, businesses, or homes could be. It was no longer necessary for a factory to be near the railroad tracks, or for a warehouse to be near the docks. It was no longer

Figure 12–2

This photograph was taken at the south end of Manhattan Island in New York City in 1895. Elevated trains and street cars, as frequently used as two-legged and four-legged means of transportation, brought about the expansion of the city.

important for every worker to live near his work, or for his work to be in the city proper. Both people and businesses began to move out into the suburbs. Sleepy villages rapidly became large towns—but without planning.

Metropolis and Megalopolis

Even without a plan for new towns, other towns and cities grow up near important cities. Rome was the mother city of many others in its region. The Greek word for mother city was *metropolis*, and many large cities have that nickname even today. Boston, New York City, Washington, D.C., Philadelphia, Chicago, St. Louis, Miami, San Francisco, Los Angeles, and many other large cities are rightly termed metropolises.

During the past 70 years, because of the automobile, we have seen the explosive growth of the *metropolitan area*. Not only have the cities surrounding any metropolis grown, but the land between them has become populated and urbanized, largely because of the automobile.

A single great urban area now extends from Boston, Massachusetts to Richmond, Virginia. It includes several once-separate metropolitan areas: the New York City urban complex (which includes parts of Connecticut and New Jersey); Philadelphia and its satellite cities, and the urban complexes of Baltimore and Washington, D.C. Nearly 40 million people live and work here. Nobody ever expected it to become this big, or to grow as fast as it did. Nobody planned for growth.

The open space in this area is rapidly shrinking. The whole region gives travelers the impression of being one giant city, although it is not quite that. It is, however, one single urban area with a single set of problems: limited water supply, air and water pollution, traffic and transportation troubles, poverty, slums, and crime.

Several years ago a new nickname was coined for this area. It was called *megalopolis*, from the Greek words for giant-sized city. The regions surrounding Chicago, Detroit, Los Angeles, San Francisco, and other important cities also show some megalopolitan characteristics.

Figure 12–3

The New York metropolitan area, seen from 12,000 feet, is only part of the densely populated megalopolis that extends from Boston to Richmond.

The Metabolism of a City

Any organism lives by the process of *metabolism*. In simple terms, this is the intake of oxygen, water, and foodstuffs, their conversion into body tissues, the extraction of energy, and the production of wastes. A city, like an organism, takes in air, water, fuels, foodstuffs, and other raw materials, lives on them, and in the end produces wastes. So a city can be said to have a metabolism.

How much of any life resource does a city need, and how much waste does it produce? There is no hard-and-fast answer. However, enough work has been done on this question so that we might take an imaginary city of one million people, and get some idea of its simple needs. Our discussion here cannot consider everything that goes into and out of a city. We shall just look at things like air, water, food, and fuel.

In one day, our imaginary city requires 2000 tons of food, 3000 tons of coal, 2800 tons of oil, 2700 tons of natural gas, and 1000 tons of motor fuel for its million people. Also, for these million, 625,000 tons of water (about 156,000,000 gallons) must come in. The average person may use only 10 gallons or so of water daily for drinking, bathing, and other personal purposes, but we are counting the individual's share of all the water the city must use.

All the fossil fuels together total 9500 tons. These will produce 950 tons of air pollutants. (The different kinds of air pollution are named in the illustration.)

The city will produce, each day, 2000 tons of refuse and garbage from its food and other solid inputs. There will be 500,000 tons of sewage, plus 120 tons of suspended solids in the sewage.

Directly or indirectly, the average person in the city, each day, uses about 150 gallons of water, 4 pounds of food, and 19 pounds of fossil fuel. Directly or indirectly, he will cause 120 gallons of sewage and 1.9 pounds of air pollutants to be produced. Our average citizen will discard 4 pounds of refuse, including food cans, bottles, paper containers, etc.

We have not counted all the raw materials that go into industry and building, or the rubbish and scrap

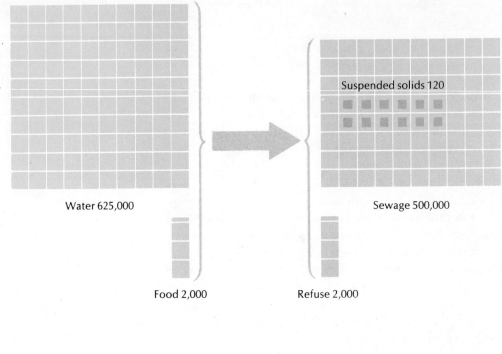

Water 625,000

Suspended solids 120

Sewage 500,000

Food 2,000

Refuse 2,000

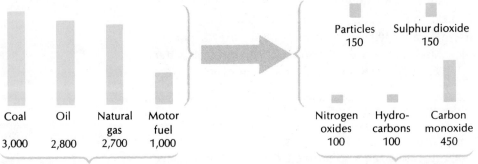

Coal	Oil	Natural gas	Motor fuel
3,000	2,800	2,700	1,000

FUEL 9,500

Particles	Sulphur dioxide
150	150

Nitrogen oxides	Hydro-carbons	Carbon monoxide
100	100	450

AIR POLLUTANTS 950

generated by these activities. Just how much of these other materials will be used depends on whether the city's main activities are heavy manufacturing, light manufacturing, grain or meat trade, and so on. Besides, we are trying to keep the discussion fairly simple.

We have not really looked at the quantity of air being used. This is not easy to measure. We have looked instead at the amount of air pollution. However, it has been estimated that one eight-cylinder automobile engine, traveling on a freeway for 1 hour, consumes more oxygen than all the people in a city the size of Los Angeles will breathe in that hour. Los Angeles has a population of 2.5 million, not counting its metropolitan area.

Figure 12–4

The input of water, food, and fuel to our hypothetical city of a million people is shown at the left. The outgo of sewage, solid wastes, and pollutants is shown at the right.

The Critical Importance
of the Water Supply

Water supply is especially critical. Take just one increasing use in cities, which is air conditioning. A single so-called 1,000 ton air conditioning unit, such as would be used for a restaurant, may use two million gallons of water in a day.

Many cities depend on wells for at least part of their water supply. This is common in the Chicago area. In this area, it used to be only necessary to sink a rather shallow well. Natural pressure would force the water to the surface. However, nowadays many of these cities are pumping their water from as deep as 2,000 feet. So much water has been taken out that the natural pressure has been lost. In many parts of the country, the water being drawn from wells is not part of the underground flow from annual rainfall. It was deposited in the deep rocks during the Ice Ages or even earlier.

Even where well water is replenished by rainfall, the rain that provides the replacement may have fallen on ground hundreds of miles away from the well. This is one more instance in which a city is not independent of the environment.

Many cities have networks of wells. However, not all cities have well-developed sewage systems. Some depend on fields of septic tanks, often one to a house, in the surface soil. In many of these cities today, contaminated water from the septic tanks has been seeping down into the wells. This means that even the well water must be treated.

Enough rain falls on the United States so that a true water shortage is not likely, even for some decades after the year 2000. The average total rainfall on the United States is about 1,200 billion gallons per day. If properly managed, this should ensure a plentiful supply for many decades to come.

Proper management will involve, however, sewage treatment and the recovery of water. Our daily 1,200 billion gallons does not fall at the right times or places to give us water wherever we want it without some effort on our part. Studies have shown that it may soon be cheaper, in many places, to treat and re-use the water from sewage than to keep reaching out, farther and farther from the cities, for new supplies.

Strangely, many communities resist the expense of sewage treatment. But practically all must treat their incoming water supply, because towns upstream on the same river are dumping sewage in. Having to treat the water supply for this reason is like treating your neighbor's sewage instead of your own.

Because of constant urban growth and a constantly expanding population, water-supply problems get increasingly more complex and expensive from year to year. Everywhere, people will have to make decisions about how much they want to pay for good water, and whether continuous growth is worth the price.

To a great extent, air, open space, and other resources are like water in their importance to the city. Like water, these resources also present some problems. There is no room here to discuss all of them. Water can be considered as a model for many city problems.

The Quality of Life

Everyone complains of cities these days, at least of very large ones, and large metropolitan areas. Something has happened to the quality of life. Many centuries ago the Greek philosopher Aristotle said that men go to cities "to lead the good life." Yet that good life gets harder and harder to find in our cities. They are too crowded, too congested, too frustrating. Every attempt has been made to permit the free flow of automobile traffic in cities, to preserve the "good life" feature of ease in getting around, in enjoying the city's variety. But the car takes up too much room and gets in the way of people. Even the variety seems to be disappearing. Cities become block upon block of apartment houses, block upon block of factories, and of stores that all finally seem alike.

Crime rates, juvenile delinquency rates, and suicide and divorce rates are high in large cities and wide metropolitan areas. In more and more cities, people feel that it is unsafe to walk outdoors at night.

Figure 12–5

One of the world's largest housing developments, located in New York City, has been vigorously attacked as being sterile and having minimal environmental and social planning.

The old values of the family and the neighborhood are lost in the gigantic, impersonal city. People do not get to know each other. In earlier times, sidewalks and streets were social gathering places for everyone, where friend could meet friend. A neighborhood was still a neighborhood. Nowadays, the streets tend to be filled with cars by day, empty of everyone but perhaps street gangs by night.

The problems of the large city also include loneliness, fear, and the effects of noise. Measured noise levels in urban areas are very high. Also, human beings miss open space, green landscapes, clear blue sky. Many scientists are pointing out that mankind has spent most of his history on earth in open land, with low noise levels, clear air, and green vegetation. The crowded, noisy, shut-in conditions that city people now accept as normal are very new for the human species.

Surprising as it may seem, all our city-building in the United States has used up very little land. About 70 percent of the American people live in urban areas, but they occupy only 1 percent of the land, including the Boston–New York–Washington megalopolis. However, on the human scale, that 1 percent is vast. People who live in large urban areas find they have to travel farther every year to reach true open space. The nearest spaces available for outdoor recreation are always crowded. The roads to these and farther places are always congested.

Also, remember that most major cities were founded in the midst of the best agricultural land of their regions. It is this land that is being covered over with asphalt and concrete, roofs, and city dumps. This waste of the best land is bound to affect the price and quality of food.

A generation ago, milk for New York City was still obtained from local lands, including nearby rural areas of New Jersey and Connecticut. Today the milk for New York comes from northern New England and several states of the Middle West. The need to haul milk for hundreds of miles makes the price higher for the consumer. Of course this is true for any food.

Several years ago the long-distance truck drivers who hauled milk to New York went out on strike. New York's people were without milk for many days. They could not walk, drive, or even take trains to the farmlands to pick up their own milk. The old city joke that "milk grows in bottles" went sour.

Social scientists and psychologists have long suspected that the high crime and delinquency rates in cities are connected with crowding and loss of open space. Suicide and divorce rates may be affected also. In fact, city life has always been more harsh in this respect than life in smaller communities. In recent years, scientists and doctors have suggested that crowding, noise, lack of friendliness, and loss of open space have unhealthy effects on everyone, and not simply on the poor in slums. These things, it is suspected, lead to some degree of nervous illness, depending on the individual. Scientists lately have been arguing about the possible similarities between the behavior of rats in overcrowded conditions in the laboratories and crime and violence in cities.

This question cannot be settled one way or the other, at least not right away. There is no way to measure how closely rat behavior is related to that of human beings, if it really is related at all. It is plain, however, that many cities have grown so large and congested that they do not meet people's deepest needs.

Toward Better Cities

Cities will always be with us. We cannot hope to rid humanity of the problems of urban living by abandoning cities. For one thing, there isn't enough true farmland for everyone to have his own farm or garden. For another, feeding the vast populations of modern countries, and the modern world, requires highly intensified agriculture— large farms, machinery, fertilizers, and pesticides. Also needed are well-developed systems of transportation, distribution, and marketing, just to get food delivered to people. This means a technological society, with factories, laboratories, schools, roads—in short, cities.

Besides, most of the highest achievements of mankind resulted from the stimulation of minds that city living brings, or from demands set by the conditions of civilized life. Science, art, literature, philosophy, even religion could not have developed the way they have without cities. Finally, it seems to be city people, as a rule,

Figure 12–6

Great cultural centers, such as Lincoln Center for the Performing Arts in New York City, are usually not possible except in large metropolitan areas where money and talent are concentrated. The building at the left is a theater for stage plays; the one in the center, an opera house; and the one at the right, a symphony hall.

who learn to appreciate nature best, and who develop a desire to protect it. The poor peasant always struggling for a living from the soil seldom respects any organism he cannot eat or sell in the village market.

So the city has to be improved, to make it a fitting habitat for man. This will take time, effort, and planning. It will mean making changes in our way of life, perhaps giving up certain things in favor of better things. It will mean remembering that human beings and their cities are parts of the natural environment, not apart from it.

Many people have worked hard and long to develop solutions for the problems of urban life. We can only sketch the main ideas here.

1. *Limits to growth.* As a city grows, it is obliged to provide more and more in the way of services such as schools, hospitals, police and fire protection, and sewers. Up to a certain point, growth helps make these things cheaper. After a certain point, new services cost more than the tax money that the newcomers will bring in. It costs the city of New York, for example, $1,000 to maintain services for each resident. A person would have to earn over $50,000 a year to owe the city $1,000 in taxes! Yet, in spite of these appalling figures, the habit of encouraging growth remains. But many cities in Europe, and some of the smaller ones in the United States, have set limits to their own growth, with no bad effects.

2. *Open space.* City planning and city policies must take the need for open space into account. Parks, playgrounds and recreation areas ought to be provided in the city itself. Some European cities have small forests within their borders, as well as parks. Keeping open space from filling up with houses or industries usually requires changes in tax policies. This will be discussed later.

3. *Green belts.* Setting aside green belts makes sure that open space survives between cities. The Romans, with their policy of planned new cities, always allowed for wide rural spaces in between to ensure a food supply, water, wood, and air. On and off since the time of England's Queen Elizabeth I, some governments have had green belt laws. These laws limit the size of new cities and set minimum distances between them. In the United

Figure 12–7
Some American cities were planned with large parks at their centers. Golden Gate Park in San Francisco extends from the Pacific Ocean half way across the center of the city. Like Central Park in New York City, it provides many recreational opportunities.

States, green belts would mean regional planning and authority, above and beyond the authority of city governments. This, too, will be discussed later.

4. *New cities, new towns.* Instead of letting cities grow to unwieldy size, the Roman custom of deliberately building new cities in empty places could be followed. Reston, Virginia, is a very pleasant small new city in a rural area near Washington, D.C. Reston has several kinds of housing, from high rise apartments to row housing to individual houses on separate lots, within easy reach of a compact shopping and entertainment center. It has a limited industrial area. Much space is devoted to parks and recreation. Its open downtown district is designed for walkers, not just automobiles. Reston even has sidewalk cafes. Some citizens of Reston work there. Others commute to Washington or Baltimore on nearby freeways. Many businessmen scoffed when Reston was being built. They said that people preferred to live in the usual kind of development where all houses are more or less alike, with everyone driving to work, shopping, or entertainment somewhere else. But the town seems to be thriving. Other new cities have had similar success.

5. *Ecological planning*. The architect Ian L. McHarg and others have developed a planning technique that helps locate new roads, housing districts, and factories where they will do least harm to the environment and give maximum long-run benefits to the community. This involves the mapping of all the things the community values, as well as the natural features of the region, on a series of overlay maps. When all these maps are put together, it becomes possible to see where the greatest benefit can be gained and the least harm done by any new building program. Experts and politicians thought this method would result in more expensive improvements, since it recognizes other values besides dollars-and-cents costs. However, in some instances millions of dollars in land purchase costs and service costs were saved by use of this method. The method has shown that having urban improvement and saving the environment need not be opposites to choose from, and that ecological solutions need not be costly.

6. *Regional or multi-city authority*. Urban sprawl can be controlled if all the cities in an area agree to make and abide by a common plan for open space, growth limits, green belts, water supply, and even things like sewage disposal. For example, each individual city may lack proper sewage treatment because treatment plants seem too expensive. But *large* treatment plants, serving several cities in a cluster, offer economies. The same principle of economy applies to regional facilities for garbage disposal, or water supply, or parks and beaches.

7. *Public transportation*. For decades, most public transportation money has gone for highways, streets, and parking lots in the hope of improving matters for the automobile. Yet most cars on a freeway at any time are carrying only one or two people. These individual cars take up more highway room than buses would. It is said that Americans are so in love with their cars that they would refuse to use buses, trains, and other public transportation. Critics also point out that New Yorkers all complain about their subway system. But the main problem with New York's and other cities' subways is

overcrowding. More trains and more routes are needed. Automobile transportation in New York and other large cities is much slower than is the subway or even walking. Given good, comfortable, cheap, public transportation, most Americans would probably use it.

8. *People before cars.* It is hard to walk around in American cities because the pedestrian has to wait at every intersection for traffic lights to change and cars to stop moving. In some places, shopping malls that exclude cars have been built and are successful. It was long said that Americans had lost the habit of walking and would always refuse to walk for shopping or business. But in the typical city shopping district, it is usually impossible to park very close to where a driver really wants to go. He ends up walking anyway.

9. *Tax policies.* To please businessmen in favor of unlimited growth, some communities apply their zoning laws to re-zone agricultural land as industrial. The farmer is then forced to pay taxes at the same rate as a big business would, and so is forced to stop farming and to sell his land. In some places, this policy is being reversed. Farmers are given a tax advantage, and so are other people who agree not to develop large tracts of land they may own. New tax policies could also discourage pollution. An industry might be taxed at one rate if it caused pollution, and have its taxes lowered for every treatment device it installed or other improvement it made.

10. *Public housing.* For many years we have heard about slum clearance, usually financed at least in part by the Federal government. But for decades, it was permissible for a city to clear its slums, but then use the land for industrial or business buildings. This left the displaced people with no new housing. So they had to crowd in somewhere else. With the crowding, that place became a slum. For a long time, there were two separate government agencies in charge of slum clearance and public housing. Now there is one Department of Housing and Urban Development, which is supposed to make sure that good housing is built, reasonably nearby, for people displaced in clearance projects.

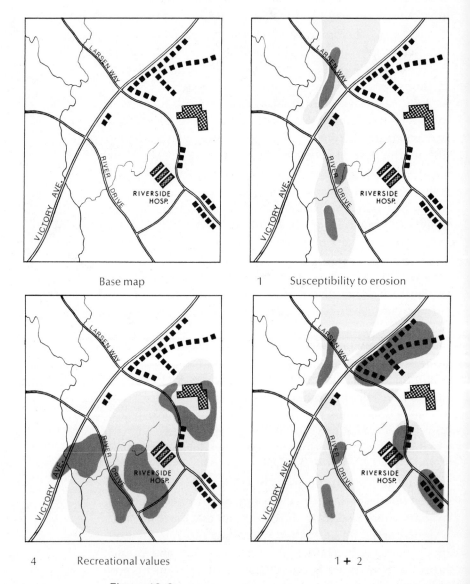

Base map

1   Susceptibility to erosion

4   Recreational values

1 + 2

Figure 12–8

In determining where to put a highway through a certain area, Ian McHarg first mapped all the other features of the area that are of value to its residents, both natural and social. Four examples are shown, with the color becoming lighter as the area

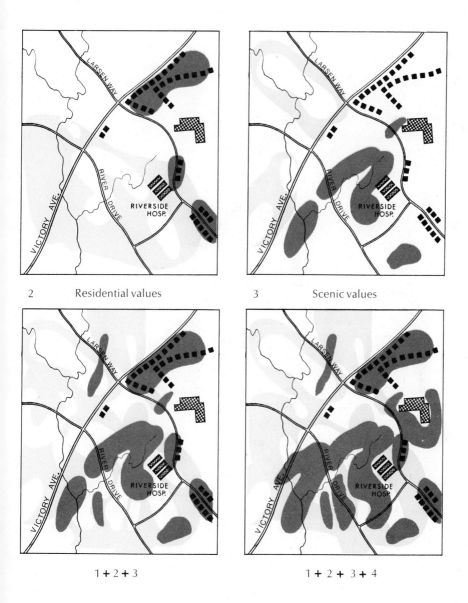

2   Residential values

3   Scenic values

1 **+** 2 **+** 3

1 **+** 2 **+** 3 **+** 4

becomes less valuable for that feature. When all the maps are
superimposed, the lightest area (in this case the upper lefthand
region) emerges as the best place to build the highway, because it is the place least valued in all other respects.

Figure 12–9
Modern rapid transit systems to serve metropolitan areas would relieve crowding on the highways and reduce air pollution. The train shown is part of such a 75-mile system in the San Francisco Bay area, which includes completely automated trains which travel quietly at 80 miles an hour.

11. *Change of attitudes.* Cities are what people make them, and so in a sense people get the kinds of cities they want and deserve. Improvements will be slow, or will fail, until people are willing to give up old attitudes. One harmful attitude, of course, is the insistence that mankind is outside the natural environment. Another is that any restriction on the growth of cities, or the kinds of buildings and services put in them, is undesirable because it interferes with the profits of businessmen. The whole community has to consider the total costs to itself, including the costs to health and survival and the quality of life, as well as fair profits for individuals. Finally, people have to give up their strange and rather new resistance to planning ahead for the needs of cities. All improvements suggested here require planning. Traditionally, cities were planned, from earliest times until less than a century ago. And sensible people plan for anything else that affects their well-being.

Unlike the natural environment, the city is our invention. We can never really improve the natural environment. We *can* improve the city. Given time, patience, work, and proper attitudes—an ecological outlook—we can make our cities fitting habitats for man.

12. *Limiting human population.* Anything that is done to save or repair the environment, and to save or improve

cities, will eventually fail if the human population keeps growing without limit. With ever-increasing numbers of people, cities must grow, more cities must be founded, and the land between them will tend to fill up and become urbanized. More farmland, and more marshes, woods, and grasslands will have to be sacrificed as urban areas grow and thicken. Control of the pollution of air and water will eventually fail, because there is a certain minimum of pollution that any animal or machine produces that cannot be eliminated. The more human animals and the more machines, the more of this pollution, even with the best of controls.

The human needs for open space, elbow room, quiet, and privacy cannot be met in cities if population density keeps increasing. Streets and transportation systems will always be overloaded if population growth does not level off.

Anyone who thinks for very long about any question in ecology, be it forests or deer or clean air or cities, sooner or later comes to feel that the rate of human population growth must be slowed down. Then, perhaps, mankind can really hope to catch up with the problems, and save the environment.

Test Yourself

1. A city is not a natural habitat, and yet it is like a natural organism. In what ways?
2. The earliest cities, in fact all cities until recently, were planned. What considerations guided planning for the location, size, and general arrangement of a city?
3. What inventions made rapid, unplanned growth of cities and urban areas possible?
4. About how much of the land area of the United States is taken up by cities or urbanized areas? Why should this make problems for people?
5. Could we get along without cities? Discuss.
6. About how old is the green belt idea? Why did it get started?

7. What lesson was learned from the map-overlay planning technique developed by Ian L. McHarg and his associates?

8. It has been suggested that the cure for urban sprawl is fewer but larger and higher buildings. This would permit the leaving of much open space between buildings. This approach has advantages. Can you think of any possible disadvantages? Discuss.

9. Ancient cities used their rivers both for water supply and for sewage disposal. Although there were occasional epidemics and plagues, this practice did not seem to matter much until a few hundred years ago. It is only in modern times that all cities everywhere find their rivers always polluted. What has made the difference? Or have there been several changes in the situation? Discuss.

10. Is it true that no American communities officially limit their growth? Have you heard of any that have?

11. One reason that cities and urban areas grow is that industries and businesses want to be near each other, and near possible markets. On the other hand, urban areas grow and sprawl because people hope to live in "open space," and so are willing to travel some distance every day for work, shopping, and entertainment. The development of modern transportation helped create this situation. Do you see any way in which modern transportation might help to solve the problems? Are any new inventions needed?

13

An Ecological Viewpoint

The Effects of Technology

Throughout modern history, Western man has assumed that he could do almost anything, if he simply made the effort to figure out a way to control the natural world. A new machine could be devised to meet any need, to solve any problem. If we needed to level a hill, create a lake, get rid of dangerous carnivores or annoying insects, we could figure out a way to do it. Life was becoming better and better. There seemed to be no limit to man's ability to improve his environment and his life. We came to consider it normal and necessary to live in a constant state of growth and change. Each generation would have more and better machines to serve it than the generation before. Each new invention was rushed into use as rapidly as it could be perfected and manufactured.

The explosion of technology in Europe and America has been astonishing. Nowhere else in the world—and at no other time in history—has man begun to make such extreme changes in his environment. The Europeans have spread their influence and example over the rest of the world. As other cultures have seen the advantages of Western technology, they have generally attempted to adjust to the same ideas and ways of life. We have seen the results in the preceding chapters. Barry Commoner,

a noted biologist, summarized the situation in the following words:

> We who call ourselves advanced claim to have escaped from . . . dependence on the environment. Where the Bushman must squeeze water from a searched-out tuber, we get ours by the turn of a tap. Instead of trackless wastes, we have the grid of city streets; instead of seeking the sun's heat when we need it, of shunning it when it is too strong, we warm ourselves and cool ourselves with man-made machines. All this tends to foster the idea that we have made our own environment and no longer depend on the one provided by nature. In the eager search for the benefits of modern science and technology, we have been enticed into a nearly fatal illusion: that we have at last escaped from the dependence of man on the balance of nature.
>
> The truth is tragically different. We have become, not less, but more dependent on the balance of nature. Modern technology has so strained the web of processes in the living environment at its most vulnerable points that there is little leeway left in the system. Unless we begin to match our technological power with a deeper understanding of the balance of nature, we run the risk of destroying this planet as a suitable place for human habitation.*

The Environmental Crisis

During the 1960's, there was a growing awareness of dangerous trends toward destruction of the environment. Threats of famine and problems of overcrowding caused some to work toward development of greater food production and others to urge population control. Many different groups used different approaches to attack the problems of air and water pollution. Garbage disposal, urban planning, freeways, pesticides and other chemicals in foods, depletion of natural resources, need for new energy sources—each of these problems attracted attention and debate about possible solutions. The traditional conservation groups were joined by new societies in their efforts to protect remaining wilderness areas and wildlife.

By the beginning of the 1970's, governmental and business leaders were responding to the growing demand for a halt to the deterioration of the environment. New laws and spending programs were being proposed and debated vigorously. New devices were suggested and even developed to solve particular parts of the problem. Magazines were filled with articles about the crisis in the environment, and with advertisements in which companies bragged about their efforts to combat pollution. The President of the United States declared: "Perhaps no single goal will be more important in our future efforts to pursue the public happiness than that of improving our environment. This goal, I believe, is one that will help define a new spirit for the Seventies, a new expression of our idealism, a new challenge that will test our ingenuity."

Despite this increasing attention to problems of the environment, things do not seem to be getting much better. For each advance made in stemming one source of pollution, several new problems are discovered. To restore the environment to a state similar to that of a few decades ago, or even to maintain it in its present state, would require expenditures many times greater than those proposed by government and industry. Continued growth of the economy, expansion of technology, and introduction of new environment-altering devices seems certain to continue at an accelerating pace.

Ecologists, and a growing body of their followers, argue that we must change our way of looking at the world. We must recognize that the human species is merely one population in a complex community. We must learn to consider all of the effects of each change that we make, recognizing that no action leads to a simple result, but that each major change produces readjustments and changes throughout the ecosystem. Most importantly, we must learn to study and consider the benefits and dangers of each change *before* we take irreversible action.

"WHAT WILL THEY DO WITH THEIR MONEY WHEN THEY RUN OUT OF AIR AND WATER?"

Some, particularly among the young, wish to go even farther. They urge a return to a very simple, nontechnological life style. They have attempted to find a way to live on small farms, avoiding the use of machines and artificial chemicals, doing everything possible to fit themselves into the ecosystem without harming it. Unfortunately, such a solution is not possible for the entire human population. The earth does not provide enough farmable land to support the present population in such a way of life. Furthermore, it seems most unlikely that most people would be willing to give up the luxuries provided by technology, and to return to a life of hard labor from dawn to dusk to keep themselves fed and housed.

It seems certain that we must learn to live with our technology. In fact, many philosophers and historians of science believe that discoveries will continue to come at an increasing pace. They feel that the nature of science and the existence of printed communications among scientists will make further increases of knowledge certain to occur. There is no way to stop scientific and technological discoveries in the future, much less to forget some of the things we have already learned.

The challenge for mankind in this age then seems to be to find an ecological viewpoint that will enable him to make use of technology without destroying his environment. Some of the components of that viewpoint seem to be clear already. They will require major—even revolutionary—changes in our ethics, morality, political and economic systems, and in international relationships. This is why one ecologist, Paul Sears, has called ecology "the subversive science." In the following sections, we shall look at some aspects of the emerging ecological viewpoint.

Thinking in Systems

In our culture, we have become accustomed to thinking in terms of causes and effects. When we do something, it causes something else to happen. If we want to understand why an event occurred, we look for the factor that caused it. Our basic model is that of the study of motion in physics. A force causes an object to speed up or slow down. If we can analyze all of the forces acting upon an object, we can predict how it will move. If we measure its movements, we can deduce the nature of the forces acting on it. It is this model that has been the basis for our actions in attempting to control nature in the past. If crop yields are poor, we find out why. We discover that insects are eating them. We then devise a way to kill the insects or keep them out of the crops. At first, the results are usually those that were expected. Later we are surprised to find that our simple action has had very complicated effects. Populations of other plants and animals have increased or decreased. Water has been polluted or the soil has been changed. The insects we wanted to get rid of have returned, in resistant strains. We did not predict these results because we did not think about the entire system. We looked at the single cause-and-effect situation in which we had an immediate interest.

It is clear that we must learn to think in terms of the entire ecosystem. We must realize that no decision is a simple one. Many aspects of each action must be considered. Experts from many different fields must be involved in studying the possible effects.

In the late 1960's, a debate went on about the advisability of constructing supersonic transports (SSTs) in the United States. Airlines and aircraft builders felt that such a high-speed airplane would be needed to meet the competition of foreign-made SSTs, and to provide the rapid transportation around the world that modern travelers demand. Under the old system, such a decision would have been based upon rather simple questions of whether such a plane could be built, how much it would cost, and whether the fares collected from passengers would pay for the expenses of building and operating the planes.

With the new awareness of the environmental crisis, however, experts in other fields examined the possible effects of the SST. Psychologists warned that the sonic booms created by the planes flying overhead might cause severe distress to millions of people living under the flight paths. Biologists warned that there might be a serious problem of exposure to radioactivity at the heights where the planes would operate. Meteorologists worried that the vapor trails created by the planes might not be dispersed by winds at these high levels in the atmosphere, and might create a new layer of ice particles in the upper atmosphere that would seriously alter the climate of the earth. Partly as a result of these environmental considerations, and partly for financial reasons, in 1971 the United States government stopped supporting development of an American SST. However, the idea has not died.

At least in this instance people began to think about the entire ecosystem. We are now aware that such a seemingly simple matter as a new type of airplane is likely to have far-reaching effects on many aspects of life on earth. It seems increasingly clear that we will have to learn to think in this way about most of the problems facing the human species today.

BELOW OLYMPUS   By Interlandi

"Yes, sir, we enjoy the highest standard of living known to the world!"

In this complex world, where changes are being made so rapidly and so extensively, we must learn to think about the results through the entire system. We have a tendency to try to avoid such complex considerations. It is much more satisfying to see things in simple black-and-white terms. "Our society is falling apart because crime and immorality are increasing; we need stricter law enforcement." Or, the "problems of today are caused by the inequalities in distribution of power. A few people run the society for their own benefit, while the majority of people suffer. We must overthrow the Establishment, and give power to the people."

These simple analyses and proposed solutions are rather like the thinking of the people who wanted to save the Kaibab deer by getting rid of the predators, or those who wished to increase food production by poisoning the insect pests. In a complex system, things are not so simple. Any change will set off a series of readjustments throughout the system. Some will probably be desirable; some will be undesirable. A logical decision about what to do can be made only if all of the interactions are studied, the possibilities considered, and the good and bad effects weighed against each other. Experiments as well as thought are needed. Desired changes have to be tried out on a small scale, just as industries try out new processes or products in small pilot plants.

Balancing Benefits and Costs

When we do consider all the effects of a change in the system, we seldom find an easy choice of right or wrong, good or bad. Each possible course of action will probably produce some benefits and some disadvantageous results.

It is clear that we need to find ways of estimating the gains and losses from each course of action, and then balancing them *before* we try to make the decision. Scientists can help to determine the probable effects of various actions. Once their opinions are available, however, a decision will still have to be made about the

the importance of various factors. We must learn to deal with these complex value judgments.

Pesticides are neither good nor evil. We must somehow decide whether it is better to risk food shortages if we cut down on our use of pesticides, or to risk environmental destruction and poisoning of human and other populations if we continue to increase our use of pesticides. We must balance these risks against other possible courses of action. Can we develop poisons that affect only the target species and that break down quickly? Can we find ways to decrease crop loss to pests without using chemical poisons at all?

It is clear that we need to gather information on all the implications of each course of action before we can make a logical decision. Yet, as a rule, people are seldom willing to wait for such information before making decisions on matters such as the SST. Why?

Internalizing Costs

Some students of the problems have suggested that the basic difficulty lies in human economic systems. Most decisions are made on the basis of cost and profit. The automobile manufacturer continues to produce cars that pollute the atmosphere because he can make a profit selling them. The chemical industries continue to produce pesticides because they can be marketed profitably. The customers buy these products because they seem to offer the best possible solutions to their difficulties at the lowest possible costs.

However, the prices considered in making these decisions do not include all the costs. The automobile manufacturer is not required to pay for the costs of cleaning up air pollution or for the damage caused by it. The citizen probably does pay for at least some of these costs, mostly through his taxes, and perhaps through medical expenses. However, these costs are not included in the price of the automobile that he buys. Since he will have to pay the taxes whether he owns a car or not, he finds it economically reasonable to buy the car. Thus the costs of air pollution are separated from decisions about producing more automobiles, and the economic system does not operate to solve the problem.

Economists call the costs of air pollution *external costs*. The whole society pays them. The person who does the damage pays no more than anyone else. The economist suggests a relatively simple solution: we should make these costs *internal* to the automotive market. For example, the government could charge the automobile manufacturers an appropriate percentage of the expenses that it suffers as a result of automobile-caused air pollution. Or the government could charge the automobile user directly by imposing a heavy tax on the purchase of an automobile or gasoline. A similar approach has been suggested for the costs of disposing of an automobile once it is junked. In such a situation, the user of the automobile would be better aware of the true costs of his actions. He might then decide that it was better to use some other kind of transportation rather than paying the high costs of the automobile.

"It Says Here We're Winning The Space Race"

Similar approaches could be used to help promote more reasonable decisions in many areas. At present, it costs industries a great deal to install devices to prevent air and water pollution caused by their activities. Until very recently, it has cost them nothing to dump polluted water into the rivers and lakes, or to add to the smog. Society in general has been paying the costs of this damage to the environment. Now the costs of pollution are being internalized in many ways. Lawsuits resulting from pollution damage may cost a company a great deal of money. New laws may impose heavy fines or taxes on polluters. Unfavorable publicity may cause the polluter to lose customers. In such ways, the industry is forced to pay at least a part of the costs of the pollution. It may then decide that it is more desirable (cheaper) to install the devices that prevent pollution.

In the long run, of course, each of us will pay the costs of the damage to the environment. Products will be more expensive if the manufacturers are forced to spend money to prevent ecological damage. If the damage is not stopped, we may pay the costs in more indirect ways, through damage to our health or through higher taxes as the government is forced to try to solve the problems.

What Can We Do?

We have touched on only a few of the aspects of an ecological viewpoint. Many others have been suggested. Clearly there are many implications about our ideas of man's place in the world, the moral right of man to harm other populations in order to improve his own lot, and the obligations of each man to the rest of the ecosystem. For example, many people are now asking whether ownership of a piece of land gives a person the right to destroy the value that land has for the human population or for other parts of the community.

Many actions are now under way to help solve various parts of the environmental crisis. Some are expensive government or industrial projects. Others involve the active participation of every citizen.

Figure 13–1

A bottle recycling center serves to cut down the volume of refuse collection, reuse the materials that make up glass, and reduce the earth's space required for solid waste disposal.

In Berkeley, California, for example, a group called Ecology Action located various industries that will purchase scrap metal, paper, glass, and other waste products in bulk quantities. Ecology Action began a campaign to collect these materials from households of the area, delivering them to the appropriate industries. In this way the materials are recycled for human use. This cuts down on the need to consume remaining natural resources, and diminishes the amount of garbage dumped into San Francisco Bay. Similar action projects now are springing up all over the country.

Every person can also exert influence upon government and industry to help encourage ecologically sound decisions. Letters from citizens help to change the minds of leaders, and to convince them that the public does want to stop the destruction of the environment. Political support can be given to candidates or elected officials who express a concern about the environment and a willingness to support ecologically based laws and government programs. Purchases can be made to support those companies taking steps to protect the environment.

Most important is the need to learn to think ecologically. The information about ecosystems given in this book has many implications about human decisions. As you think about the ecological processes going on in your garden, your city, the nation, and the world, you will find your attitudes and perceptions changing. When you think of yourself as one organism in the human population, which in turn is only one link in a complex ecosystem, you will begin to develop a new ecological viewpoint. Then no one will need to tell you what to do.

Test Yourself

1. How does an ecological viewpoint differ from our usual approach to problems or to goals?
2. From what you have read in this chapter, why is it that modern man turns out to be more, not less, dependent on the balance of nature than primitive man was?

3. What are external costs? What is meant by making a cost (such as the cost of the results of pollution) internal?

4. Who, in the long run, pays the costs of all damage to the environment? Why? Suppose we try to avoid the costs of repairs and just accept the damage? Are we free of payment?

5. Why has one ecologist called ecology "the subversive science?" If it is that, would you say it is or is not unpatriotic to insist on ecological solutions to various problems?

6. Is there any value to the preservation of species or wilderness areas that seem to have no economic value to man? For example, should we be concerned about the threatened disappearance of a species of fish that nobody eats? Why, or why not?

7. Suppose that ways are found to feed the human population, to end air and water pollution, and to drastically reduce our consumption of nonrenewable natural resources. Would the human race then be living in a stable balance in the ecosystem? What other difficulties might remain to be solved? In what ways could we reach the state described?

Additional Readings

The books and articles listed below represent just a few of the many sources for further information and ideas. The following key has been used to suggest the level of difficulty of each book, according to the audience for which it was written: JH = junior high school; SH = senior high school; C = college; and P = a popular book for the general public.

General Discussions of Ecology

Biological Sciences Curriculum Study. 1968. *High School Biology*. Skokie, Ill.: Rand McNally & Company. Hardbound. (A well-written textbook covering most biological concepts, with emphasis upon ecology. SH.)

Ehrlich, Paul R. and Anne H. Ehrlich. 1970. *Population Resources Environment*. San Francisco: W. H. Freeman and Company. 383 pp. Hardbound. (An excellent basic text in environmental problems and their relation to population. SH, C.)

Farb, Peter, and the Editors of Life. 1963. *Ecology*. New York: Time, Inc. (Life Nature Library). 192 pp. Hardbound. (An excellent, easy-to-read survey of ecology with superb illustrations. P.)

Kormody, Edward J. 1969. *Concepts of Ecology*. Englewood Cliffs, N.J.: Prentice-Hall, Inc. 209 pp. Hardbound and paperbound. (This book emphasizes recent studies of human ecology and the terrestrial ecosystems of North America. SH, C.)

Milne, Lorus, and Margery Milne. 1971. *The Nature of Life: Earth, Plants, Animals, Man and Their Effect on Each Other*. N.Y.: Crown Publishers. 320 pp. Hardbound. (A description of the ever-changing earth and its many landforms, waters, and plant and animal populations. SH, C.)

Nickelsburg, Janet. 1969. *Ecology: Habitats, Niches, and Food Chains*. Philadelphia: J.B. Lippincott Company. 128 pp. Hardbound. (A simple introduction to ecology with many examples and a good bibliography. JH, SH.)

Odum, Eugene P. 1963. *Ecology*. New York: Holt, Rinehart & Winston, Inc. 152 pp. Paperbound. (A simple review of ecology with emphasis on the human situation; reading lists for each chapter. SH, C.)

Storer, John H. 1953. *The Web of Life: A First Book of Ecology*. New York: New American Library, Inc. Paperbound. (A very readable, simple overview of ecology. SH, P.)

Chapters 1-6: Ecological Principles

Buchsbaum, Ralph, and Mildred Buchsbaum. 1957. *Basic Ecology*. Pittsburgh: Boxwood Press. 195 pp. Hardbound or paperback. (A simple introduction to the study of communities, with an extensive bibliography. JH, SH.)

Carson, Rachel L. 1962. *Silent Spring*. Boston: Houghton Mifflin Company. 368 pp. Hardbound or paperback. (This very readable study of pesticide pollution was probably largely responsible for the current interest in the environment. P.)

Cole, L. C. 1952. "The ecosphere," in *Scientific American*, April. Also available as Offprint No. 144 from W. H. Freeman & Company, San Francisco. Also included in Hardin (1968).

Dudley, Ruth H. 1965. *Partners in Nature*. New York: Funk & Wagnalls Company. 192 pp. Hardbound. (A simple discussion of beneficial relationships among organisms. JH, SH.)

Graham, Frank, Jr. 1970. *Since Silent Spring*. Boston: Houghton Mifflin Company. 333 pp. Hardbound. (A summary of action on pesticide pollution problems since the publication of Rachael Carson's book. P.)

Elton, Charles S. 1942. *Voles, Mice and Lemmings: Problems in Population Dynamics*. Oxford: Clarendon Press. Hardbound. (A classic study of changes in animal populations. SH, C.)

Elton, Charles S. 1958. *The Ecology of Invasions by Animals and Plants*. New York:

John Wiley & Sons, Inc. Hardbound. (Short, simple, and classic study of changes in populations and communities. SH. C.)

Farb, Peter. 1959. *The Living Earth.* New York: Harper & Row, Publishers, Inc. 178 pp. Hardbound or paperback. (A study of the community in the soil. SH, P.)

Grossman, Shelly. 1967. *The Struggle for Life in the Animal World.* New York: Grosset & Dunlap, Inc. 128 pp. Hardbound. (Well-illustrated discussion of animal and plant relationships, with emphasis on predator-prey relationships. JH, SH.)

Hardin, Garrett (introductions by). 1968. *39 Steps to Biology: Readings from Scientific American.* San Francisco: W. H. Freeman & Company. 344 pp. Hardbound or paperback. (A collection of articles from the magazine, containing several relevant to topics treated in this book. SH, C, P.)

Hirsch, S. Carl. 1966. *The Living Community: A Venture Into Ecology.* New York: The Viking Press. 128 pp. Hardbound. (An introduction to ecology, emphasizing the community. JH, SH.)

Raskin, Edith. 1967. *The Pyramid of Living Things.* New York: McGraw-Hill Book Company. 192 pp. Hardbound. (A very enjoyable description of the ecological pyramids in many different biomes. JH, SH.)

Shuttlesworth, Dorothy. 1969. *Natural Partnerships: The Story of Symbiosis.* Garden City, N.Y.: Doubleday & Company, Inc. 64 pp. Hardbound. (Many examples of mutualism, parasitism, and commensalism, with interesting discussion and excellent illustrations. JH.)

Zinsser, Hans. 1954. *Rats, Lice and History.* Boston: Little, Brown & Company. Hardbound or paperback. (A fascinating discussion of man's relationships with some parasites and other creatures. P.)

Chapter 7: Freshwater Ecosystems

Amos, William H. 1970. *The Infinite River: A biologist's Vision of the World of Water.* New York: Random House, Inc. 269 pp. Hardbound. (A treatment of the river, the estuary, the bay, and the offshore ocean unified by the general theme of water. SH, C.)

Amos, William H. 1967. *The Life of the Pond.* New York: McGraw-Hill Book Company. 232 pp. Hardbound. (A superb and well-illustrated study of the pond ecosystem. JH, SH, P.)

Bardach, John. 1964. *Downstream: A Natural History of the River.* New York: Harper & Row, Publishers, Inc. 278 pp. Hardbound. (A study of the nature and ecology of streams, and man's use of and problems with rivers. SH, C.)

Clark, John R. 1969. "Thermal pollution and aquatic life," in *Scientific American,* March.

Klots, Elsie B. 1966. *The New Field Book of Freshwater Life.* New York: G. P. Putnam's Sons. 398 pp. Hardbound. (A well-written and superbly illustrated handbook for the study of freshwater ecosystems. JH, SH, C.)

Popham, E. J. 1961. *Life in Fresh Water.* Cambridge, Mass.: Harvard University Press. Hardbound. (An excellent introduction to freshwater ecology, giving a detailed account of a long-term study of an actual pond. SH, C.)

Powers, Charles F., and Andrew Robertson. 1966. "The aging Great Lakes," in *Scientific American,* November. (An account of man's effects on lake ecosystems.) Also available as Offprint No. 1056 from W. H. Freeman & Company, San Francisco.

Usinger, R. L. *Life of Rivers and Streams.* New York: McGraw-Hill Book Company. 232 pp. Hardbound. (A well-written and superbly illustrated account of ecosystems in moving fresh waters. JH, SH, P.)

Chapter 8: Ocean Ecosystems

Amos, William H. 1966. *Life of the Seashore.* New York: McGraw-Hill Book Company. 232 pp. Hardbound. (A well-written and superbly illustrated account of the ecosystems of the shoreline. JH, SH, P.)

Berrill, N. J. 1966. *The Life of the Ocean*. New York: McGraw-Hill Book Company. 232 pp. Hardbound. (A well-written and superbly illustrated study of the ocean ecosystems. JH, SH, P.)

Carson, Rachael. 1955. *The Edge of the Sea*. Boston: Houghton Mifflin Company. 238 pp. Hardbound or paperback. (A very readable account of the seashore communities. P.)

Carson, Rachael. 1961. *The Sea Around Us*. Revised edition. New York: Oxford University Press. 237 pp. Hardbound or paperback. (A general study of the oceans, including the living things. P.)

Engel, Leonard, and the Editors of Life. 1961. *The Sea*. New York: Time, Inc. (Life Nature Library). 190 pp. Hardbound. (Well-illustrated introduction to the oceans, including marine ecosystems. P.)

Holt, S. J. 1969. "The food resources of the ocean," in *Scientific American*, September. Also in *The Ocean, A Scientific American Book* (1969).

Isaacs, John D. 1969. "The nature of oceanic life," in *Scientific American*, September. Also in *The Ocean, A Scientific American Book* (1969).

Kylstra, Johannes A. 1968. "Experiments in water-breathing," in *Scientific American*, August. (Experiments which suggest the possibility that man might one day be able to live in the oceans without an air supply.)

Marx, Wesley. 1967. *The Frail Ocean*. New York: Coward McCann, Inc. 274 pp. Hardbound or paperback. (A very readable account of man's alterations of the marine ecosystems. P.)

Scientific American. 1969. *The Ocean*. San Francisco: W. H. Freeman & Company. 128 pp. Hardbound or paperback. (A collection of articles from the September 1969 issue of the magazine, summarizing current knowledge of all aspects of the oceans and their life. SH, C, P.)

Chapter 9: Land Ecosystems

Allen, Durward L. 1967 *The Life of Prairies and Plains*. New York: McGraw-Hill Book Company. 232 pp. Hardbound. (A well-written and superbly illustrated study of the ecology of the grasslands of central North America, before and since the coming of man. JH, SH, P.)

Berrill, N. J., and M. Berrill. 1969. *Life of Sea Islands*. New York: McGraw-Hill Book Company. 232 pp. Hardbound. (Life on islands has provided many important clues to the nature of evolutionary changes; this is a well-written a superbly illustrated study of island ecosystems. JH, SH, P.)

Brooks, Maurice. 1967. *The Life of the Mountains*. New York: McGraw-Hill Book Company. 232 pp. Hardbound. (A study of the environments and communities of the mountain regions of North America, with superb illustrations. JH, SH, P.)

Costello, David. 1969. *The Prairie World*. New York: Thomas Y. Crowell Company. 242 pp. Hardbound. (A survey of the American grassland ecosystem, with emphasis upon the plant populations and their changes. JH, SH.)

Farb, Peter, and the Editors of Life. 1961. *The Forest*. New York: Time, Inc. (Life Nature Library). Hardbound. (A superb introduction to the forest ecosystem, with excellent text and illustrations. P.)

Leopold, A. Starker, and the Editors of Life. 1961. *The Desert*. New York: Time, Inc. (Life Nature Library). Hardbound. (A well-illustrated survey of all aspects of the desert, including its communities. P.)

Ley, Willy, and the Editors of Life. 1962. *The Poles*. New York: Time, Inc. (Life Nature Library). Hardbound. (A well-illustrated account of life and exploration in the Artic and Antarctic regions. P.)

Love, R. Merton. 1970. "The rangelands of the western U.S.," in *Scientific American*, February.

McCormick, Jack. 1966. *The Life of the Forest*. New York: McGraw-Hill Book Company. 232 pp. Hardbound. (A well-written and superbly illustrated account of the forest ecosystem. JH, SH, P.)

Mohr, Charles E., and T. Poulsons. 1967. *Life of the Cave.* New York: McGraw-Hill Book Company. 232 pp. Hardbound. (A well-written and superbly illustrated account of the unusual ecosystems existing in caverns. JH, SH, P.)

Niering, W. A. 1967. *Life of the Marsh.* New York: McGraw-Hill Book Company. 232 pp. Hardbound. (A well-written and superbly illustrated account of the marsh ecosystem. JH, SH, P.)

Sears, Paul B. 1969. *Lands Beyond the Forest.* Englewood Cliffs, N.J.: Prentice-Hall, Inc. 206 pp. Hardbound. (A study of the ecology of land biomes other than the forest, with additional information on all aspects of the land and man's use of it. SH, C.)

Sears, Paul B. 1966. *The Living Landscape.* New York: Basic Books, Inc. 199 pp. Hardbound. (A survey of the living communities across the land. JH, SH, P.)

Sutton, Amy, and Myron Sutton. 1966. *Life of the Desert.* New York: McGraw-Hill Book Company. 232 pp. Hardbound. (A well-written and superbly illustrated account of the desert ecosystem. JH, SH, P.)

Chapter 10: Conservation

Allen, Durward L. 1962. *Our Wildlife Legacy.* Revised edition. New York: Funk & Wagnalls Company. 422 pp. Hardbound. (A discussion of ecological principles of wildlife management and land use, with bibliography. C, P.)

Battan, Louis J. 1966. *The Unclean Sky: A Meteorologist Looks at Air Pollution.* Garden City, N.Y.: Doubleday & Company, Inc. 141 pp. Paperback. (A study of the problems of air pollution, the causes, and possible solutions. SH.)

Blake, Peter. 1964. *God's Own Junkyard: The Planned Deterioration of America's Landscape.* New York: Holt, Rinehart & Winston, Inc. 144 pp. Hardbound or paperback. (A well-illustrated study of the destruction of beauty in our environment. P.)

Bregman, J. I., and Sergei Lenormand. 1966. *The Pollution Paradox.* Washington, D.C.: Spartan. 191 pp. Hardbound. (A brief discussion of various kinds of pollution, with extensive information on ways that citizens can do something about it. SH, P.)

Breinard, John W. 1971. *Nature Study for Conservation: A Handbook for Environmental Education.* New York: The Macmillan Company. 353 pp. (A wealth of nature lore, science, and challenge to personal involvement. SH, C.)

Clawson, Marion. 1963. *Land for Americans: Trends, Prospects, and Problems.* Chicago: Rand McNally & Company. 141 pp. Hardbound. (A discussion of the problems of land use and prospects for the future. This is a summary and simplification of a 570-page book called *Land for the Future,* by Clawson, Held, and Stoddard, available from John Hopkins Press. SH, C.)

Colwell, Robert N. 1968. "Remote sensing of natural resources," in *Scientific American*, January. (Photography from planes and satellites may help in locating new sources of various natural resources.)

Darling, F. F., and J. P. Milton (editors). 1966. *Future Environments of North America.* Garden City, N.Y.: Natural History Press. 767 pp. Hardbound. (An exploration of the "strained balance between man and nature," with projections of future possibilities. P.)

Dasmann, Raymond F. 1965. *The Destruction of California.* New York: The Macmillan Company. 223 pp. Hardbound or paperback. (A wide-ranging look at conservation and other problems in America's fastest-growing state. P.)

Dasmann, Raymond F. 1968. *A Different Kind of Country.* New York: The Macmillan Company. 276 pp. Hardbound. (A discussion of man's relationship to his environment, urging the preservation of diversity within all ecosystems as well as in human culture. C, P.)

Douglas, William O. 1965. *A Wilderness Bill of Rights.* Boston: Little, Brown & Company. 192 pp. Hardbound or paperback. (A proposal for a plan of wilderness preservation by an Associate Justice of the U.S. Supreme Court, with discussion of conservation principles and practices. P.)

Edwards, Clive A. 1969. "Soil pollutants and soil animals," in *Scientific American,* April.

Fisher, James, Noel Simon, and Jack Vincent. 1969. *Wildlife in Danger.* New York: The Viking Press. 368 pp. Hardbound. (A survey of animal species threatened with extinction in the near future. SH, C.)

General Drafting Company. 1968. *Man's Domain: A Thematic Atlas of the World.* New York: McGraw-Hill Book Company. 75 pp. Paperback. (A very useful little book with maps showing the distribution of all kinds of resources over the world. JH, SH, C, P.)

Harrison, C. William. 1969. *Forests: Riches of the Earth.* New York: Julian Messner, Inc. 191 pp. Hardbound. (A simple and well-illustrated survey of our forest resources. JH.)

Helfman, Elizabeth S. 1962. *Land, People, and History.* New York: David McKay Company, Inc. 271 pp. Hardbound. (A review of the importance of soil conservation throughout human history. JH, SH.)

Laycock, George. 1969. *America's Endangered Wildlife.* New York: W. W. Norton & Company, Inc. 226 pp. Hardbound. (The serious problems of wildlife conservation in our country today. SH, C.)

McClung, Robert M. 1969. *Lost Wild America: The Story of Our Extinct and Vanishing Wildlife.* New York: William Morrow & Company, Inc. 240 pp. Hardbound. (An excellent ecological approach to the problems of wildlife conservation. JH, SH.)

Rienow, Robert, and Leona Train Rienow. 1967. *Moment in the Sun.* New York: Dial Press. 365 pp. Hardbound or paperback. (A powerful summary of the environmental problems facing the human population today. P.)

Roueche, Berton. 1968. *What's Left: Reports on a Diminishing America.* Boston: Little, Brown & Company. 210 pp. Hardbound. (A study of several unspoiled locations which are targets for conservation or exploitation. SH, C, P.)

Smith, Frank E. 1966. *The Politics of Conservation.* New York: Pantheon. 338 pp Hardbound. (The story of the political problems involved in conservation efforts. SH, C, P.)

Strong, Douglas H. 1971. *The Conservationists.* Menlo Park, Calif.: Addison-Wesley Publishing Company, Inc. 196 pp. Paperback. (A readable account of the contributions of ten of America's leading conservationists. JH, SH, P.)

Udall, Stewart L. 1963. *The Quiet Crisis.* New York: Rinehart & Winston, Inc. 209 pp. Hardbound or paperback. (A history of natural resources and conservation in America, with comments about the future. P.)

Chapter 11: The Human Population

Borgstrom, Georg. 1965. *The Hungry Planet: The Modern World at the Edge of Famine.* New York: The Macmillan Company. 480 pp. Hardbound or paperback. (A leading authority on world nutrition summarizes the facts which imply that the exploding population will soon run out of food. SH, C, P.)

Borgstrom, Georg. 1969. *Too Many: A Study of Earth's Biological Limitations.* New York: The Macmillan Company. 368 pp. Hardbound. (Borgstrom updates, supplements, and extends the information in his 1965 book.)

Calhoun, John B. 1962. "Population density and social pathology," in *Scientific American,* February.

Cochrane, Willard W. 1969. *The World Food Problem: A Guardedly Optimistic View.* New York: Thomas Y. Crowell Company. 331 pp. Hardbound. (A good source of statistics on world food problems. The author concludes that there is some hope of supplying food for the population, if the growth rate can be reduced in the near future. SH, C.)

Curtis, Byrd C., and David R. Johnston. 1969. "Hybrid wheat," in *Scientific American*, May. (New types of plants offer some hope for increased food production.)

Day, Lincoln H., and Alice Taylor Day. 1964. *Too Many Americans*. Boston: Houghton Mifflin Company. 298 pp. Hardbound or paperback. (A discussion of the population problem in this country, with bibliography. SH, P.)

Deevey, E. S. 1956. "The human crop," in *Scientific American*, April.

Deevey, E. S. 1960. "The human population," in *Scientific American*, September, Also available as Offprint No. 608 from W. H. Freeman & Company, San Francisco.

Dubos, René, Maya Pines, and the Editors of Time-Life Books. 1968. *Health and Disease*. Revised edition. New York: Time-Life Books. 200 pp. Hardbound. (A very readable discussion with excellent illustrations of man's struggle against disease. P.)

Dumont, René, and Bernard Rosier. 1969. *The Hungry Future*. New York: Praeger. 271 pp. Hardbound. (A report on future food shortages and ways that they might be avoided. SH, C.)

Ehrlich, Paul R. 1968. *The Population Bomb*. San Francisco: The Sierra Club. 224 pp. Hardbound or paperback. (A controversial book arguing strongly that human population growth must be halted if we are to survive. P.)

Ehrlich, Paul R. 1969. "Eco-catastrophe!" in *Ramparts*, September. Also published as a booklet by City Lights Books, San Francisco. (One possible scenario for a disaster caused by human population growth.)

Huxley, Julian. 1956. "World population," in *Scientific American*, March. Also available as Offprint No. 616 from W. H. Freeman & Company, San Francisco.

Malthus, Thomas, Julian Huxley, and Frederick Osborn. 1960. *On Population: Three Essays*. New York: New American Library, Inc. 144 pp. Paperback. (Malthus' classic study of population problems, with two modern essays on the same subject. SH, C.)

McMillen, Wheeler. 1965. *Bugs or People?* Des Moines, Iowa: Meredith Press. 228 pp. Hardbound. (The author suggests that pesticides can and must be used to help increase food production, and that pollution can be minimized. SH, P.)

Paddock, William, and Paul Paddock. 1967. *Famine—1975! America's Decision: Who Will Survive?* Boston: Little, Brown & Company. 276 pp. Hardbound or paperback. (A study of the world food supply, predicting widespread famine in the near future. P.)

Pirie, N. W. 1967. "Orthodox and unorthodox methods of meeting world food needs," in *Scientific American*.

Population Bulletin. Published by the Population Reference Bureau, Inc., 1755 Massachusetts Avenue, N.W., Washington, D.C. 20036. (Contains the latest population statistics and many articles related to population problems.)

Vogt, William. 1960. *People! Challenge to Survival*. New York: William Sloane Associates. 257 pp. Hardbound. (The population problem dramatically viewed in examples from travel around the world and the United States. SH, C.)

Zeigler, Philip. 1969. *The Black Death*. New York: The John Day Company. 319 pp. Hardbound. (A readable and thorough account of the bubonic plague which killed perhaps one third of the population of Europe in the mid-14th century. SH, C.)

Chapter 12: The Ecology of Cities

Abrams, Charles, 1965. "The uses of land in cities." In Scientific American, September. Also in *Cities, A Scientific American* Book (1965).

Blumenfeld, Hans. 1965. "The modern metropolis." In *Scientific American*, September. Also in *Cities, A Scientific American* Book (1965).

Bose, Nirmal Kumar, 1965. "Calcutta: a premature metropolis." In *Scientific American*. Also in *Cities, A Scientific American* Book (1965).

Chinitz, Benjamin. 1965. New York: "A metropolitan region." In *Scientific American*, September. Also in *Cities, A Scientific American* Book (1965).

Davis, Kingsley. 1965. "The urbanization of the human population." In *Scientific American*, September. Also in *Cities*, A *Scientific American* Book (1965).

Dyckman, John W. 1965. "Transportation in cities." In *Scientific American*, September. Also in *Cities*, A *Scientific American* Book (1965).

Glazer, Nathan, 1965. "The renewal of cities." In *Scientific American*, September. Also in *Cities*, A *Scientific American* Book (1965).

Halacy, D. S., Jr. 1966. *The Water Crisis*. New York: E.P. Dutton & Company, Inc. 192 pp. Hardbound. (An interesting account of the many aspects of man's problems with water resources. JH, SH, C.)

Leinwand, Gerald. 1970. *The City as a Community*. New York: Washington Square Press. 192 pp. Paperbound. (A readable account of contemporary urban problems and how they might be solved. P.)

Lynch, Kevin. 1965. "The city as environment." In *Scientific American*, September. Also in *Cities*, A *Scientific American* Book (1965).

McHarg, Ian L. 1969. *Design with Nature*. Garden City, N.Y.: Natural History Press. 197 pp. Hardbound and paperbound. (An extremely interesting discussion of ways to use principles of ecology in designing communities and buildings. C, P.)

Rodwin, Lloyd. 1965. "Ciudad Guayana: a new city." In *Scientific American*, September. Also in *Cities*, A *Scientific American* Book (1965).

Scientific American. 1965. *Cities*. New York: Alfred A. Knopf. 128 pp. Hardbound or paperback. (A collection of articles from the September 1965 issue of the magazine, all of which are listed in this bibliography.)

Sidenbladh, Goran. 1965. "Stockholm: a planned city." In *Scientific American*, September. Also in *Cities*, A *Scientific American* Book (1965).

Sjoberg, Gideon. 1965. "The origin and evolution of cities." In *Scientific American*, September. Also in *Cities*, A *Scientific American* Book (1965).

Sommer, Robert. 1969. *Personal Space: The Behavioral Basis of Design*. Englewood Cliffs, N.J.: Prentice-Hall, Inc. 177 pp. Paperback. (An interesting example of the application of human ecology to problems of architectural design. SH, C.)

Vayda, Andrew P. (editor). 1969. *Environment and Cultural Behavior*. Garden City, N.Y.: Natural History Press. 485 pp. Hardbound. (A collection of acticles discussing human culture from an ecological viewpoint. C, P.)

Wolman, Abel. 1965. "The metabolism of cities." In *Scientific American*, September. Also in *Cities*, A *Scientific American* Book (1965).

Chapter 13: An Ecological Viewpoint

Boulding, Kenneth E. 1964. *The Meaning of the 20th Century: The Great Transition*. New York: Harper & Row, Publishers, Inc. 208 pp. Hardbound or paperback. (Boulding argues that the period of civilization has been a temporary stage in human history, and that we are now moving into a stage of post-civilization in which we will re-establish an ecological balance.)

Commoner, Barry. 1966. *Science & Survival*. New York: The Viking Press. 150 pp. Hardbound or paperback. (Commoner urges every citizen to take an active part in exercising moral judgment and political choice to reach ecologically sound decisions in the face of the great problems created by our technology.)

Cotton, Steve (editor). 1970. *Earth Day–The Beginning*. New York: Bantam Books. 233 pp. (A collection of 50 addresses made by students and others on April 22, 1970, the original Earth Day. JH, SH, C.)

Eiseley, Loren. 1969. *The Unexpected Universe*. New York: Harcourt, Brace & World, Inc. 239 pp. Hardbound. (Thoughts on the meaning of human existence in this natural world, by a man who has spent his life studying biology and evolution.)

Fuller, Buckminster. 1969. *Operating Manual for Spaceship Earth*. Carbondale, Ill.: Southern Illinois University Press. 143 pp. Hardbound. (A summary of the thinking of a great planner, architect, and philosopher.)

The Futurist. Published bi-monthly by the World Future Society, P.O. Box 19285, 20th Street Station, Washington, D.C. 20036. Contains many articles on possibilities and plans for the future, some of them ecologically based.

Herbert, Frank. 1965. *Dune.* New York: Ace Books, Inc. 544 pp. Paperback. (A science-fiction novel exploring many ecological concepts.)

Johnson, Huey D. (editor). 1970. *No Deposit—No Return.* Reading, Mass.: Addison-Wesley Publishing Company, Inc. 351 pp. Paperbound. (A collection of readable papers given by eminent environmentalists at the UNESCO conference on the environment in 1969.)

Lao Tsu. About 500 B.C. *Tao Teh King.* (Translated and interpreted by Archie Bahm). New York: Frederick Ungar Publishing Company, 1958. 126 pp. Paperback. (This classic of Chinese religious philosophy has an ecologically balanced and harmonious feeling, which is emphasized in Bahm's interpretation.)

Leopold, Aldo. 1966. *A Sand County Almanac, with Other Essays on Conservation from Round River.* New York: Oxford University Press. Hardbound. (Superbly enjoyable comments by a famed conservationist on his experiences with nature, and the implications of an ecological world view. A classic, and a book that everyone should read.)

Mitchell, John A., and Constance Statlings (editors). 1970. *Ecotactics: The Sierra Club Handbook for Environmental Activists.* New York: Simon & Schuster. Paperbound.

Roth, Charles E. 1971. *The Most Dangerous Animal in the World.* Reading, Mass.: Addison-Wesley Publishing Company, Inc. 128 pp. (A short, readable, and well-illustrated book that raises a variety of issues in human ecology. P.)

Schwenk, Theodor. 1965. *Sensitive Chaos.* London: Rudolf Steiner Press. 144 pp. Hardbound. (A strange combination of ecology and mysticism in the discussion of the flow of water and air.)

Scientific American, *Readings From Man and the Ecosphere.* 1971. (With commentaries by Paul R. Ehrlich, John P. Holdren, and Richard W. Holm.) San Francisco: W. H. Freeman and Co. (A collection of 27 readings from *Scientific American* that deal with man's interactions with the ecosphere.)

Snow, C. P. 1969. *The State of Siege.* New York: Charles Scribner's Sons. 50 pp. Hardbound. (A lecture on present world problems by a famed student of science.)

Snyder, Gary. 1966. *Earth House Hold.* New York: New Directions Publishing. Corporation. 143 pp. Hardbound or paperback. (A poet and writer associated with the beat and "hippy" movements talks about ecology and travel.)

Watts, Alan. 1966. *The Book: On the Taboo Against Knowing Who You Are.* New York: Pantheon Books (Random House, Inc.). 146 pp. Hardbound or paperback. (An attempt to combine eastern philosophies/religions with insights of ecology and psychology to create a new philosophical and ethical outlook for western man.)

Whole Earth Catalog: Access to Tools. Published by Portola Institute, 558 Santa Cruz Avenue, Menlo Park, California 94025. (A listing of books and other tools of use to the individual trying to learn to exist more in harmony with his environment.)

Wiener, Norbert. 1954. *The Human Use of Human Beings.* Revised edition. Boston: Houghton Mifflin Company. 199 pp. Hardbound or paperback. (The concepts of cybernetics, a science dealing with communication and control, are closely related to the systems concepts of ecology. In this very readable book, the founder of cybernetics discusses the implications of his theories for mankind.

Van Sickle, Dirck. 1971. *Ecological Citizen: Pollution Survival and Activist's Handbook.* New York: Harper and Row, Publishers, Inc. Paperbound.

Index

Acknowledgments

Illustrative artwork: Thelma Norian
Charts and maps: Basil C. Wood
Cover photo courtesy National Aeronautics and Space Administration

p. viii, © Walt Kelly. Courtesy of Publishers-Hall Syndicate; p. 4, left, Rue from National Audubon Society; right, Miller from National Audubon Society; 1-2, U.S. Forest Service; 2-2, left, Grant Heilman; right, Soil Conservation Service; 2-4, left, Halliday from National Audubon Society; right, Maslowski from National Audubon Society; 2-6, top, Halliday from National Audubon Society; bottom, Gerard from National Audubon Society; 2-7, Spencer from National Audubon Society; 2-8, Hermes from National Audubon Society; 2-9, Chace from National Audubon Society; 2-10, Ott from National Audubon Society; 3-3, Grant Heilman; 4-2, Soil Conservation Service; 4-4, Dermid from National Audubon Society; 4-5, Grant Heilman; 5-5, left, Hoskin from National Audubon Society; right, Slaffan from National Audubon Society; p. 67, Vahan Shirvanian, Copyright © 1970 Saturday Review, Inc.; 5-7, top, Ott from National Audubon Society; bottom, Rue from National Audubon Society; 5-9, left, Rue from National Audubon Society; right, Beilfeld from National Audubon Society; 6-2, top, Pitcairn from Grant Heilman; middle and bottom, Grant Heilman; 6-3, Grant Heilman; 6-4, Soil Conservation Service; 6-5, Franklin Gress; p. 95, M.C. Escher, courtesy Vorpal Galleries; 7-4, Grant Heilman; 7-5, Williams from National Audubon Society; 7-7, Hunn from National Audubon Society; 8-3, Douglas P. Wilson; 8-5, Douglas P. Wilson; 8-6, top left, Grant Heilman; top right, Fisher from National Audubon Society; bottom, Harrison from Grant Heilman; 8-7, American Museum of Natural History; 8-8, top, Allan Hancock Foundation; 8-10, Douglas P. Wilson; 8-11, Runk/Schoenberger from Grant Heilman; 8-12, left, American Museum of Natural History; right, National Institute of Oceanography, England; 8-13, top, American Museum of Natural History; bottom, Komorowski from National Audubon Society; 9-3, Bureau of Sport Fisheries and Wildlife; 9-4, South Dakota Dept. of Game, Fish and Parks; 9-5, Pitcairn from Grant Heilman; 9-6, U.S. Forest Service; 9-7, Graham from National Audubon Society; 10-1, American Museum of Natural History; 10-2, U.S. Forest Service; 10-3, Soil Conservation Service; 10-4, Wide World; 10-5, Wide World; 12-2, The J. Clarence Davies Collection, Museum of the City of New York; 12-5, Wide World; 12-6, Serating from Lincoln Center for the Performing Arts; 12-7, James F. Lee; 12-9, Bay Area Rapid Transit District; p. 220, NASA; p. 222, Copyright © 1968 Chicago Sun-Times, reproduced by courtesy of Wil-Jo Associates, Inc. and Bill Mauldin; p. 225, Copyright © 1970 by Los Angeles Times, Reprinted with Permission; p. 228, Copyright © 1969 by Herblock in The Washington Post; 13-1, Wide World.